ASSYRIA

LANDS
OF THE
BIBLE

Euphrates R.

Tigris R.

BABYLONIA

Ur

Arabian
Desert

PERSIAN GULF

Jewish Heroes BOOK ONE

Jewish

Heroes BOOK ONE

by Sadie Rose Weilerstein

Illustrations by Lili Cassel

United Synagogue Commission on
Jewish Education

NEW YORK 5719-1959

FIRST PRINTING — 1953
SECOND PRINTING — 1956
THIRD PRINTING — 1959

TO Ruth AND Alex

Acknowledgments

THERE ARE many to whom I am indebted for help in the preparation of this book. Dr. Abraham E. Millgram has worked closely with me at every stage of its preparation, giving me the benefit of his insights and his wide experience. He has given unstintingly of his time and effort. I am deeply grateful for his help and his unfailing kindness and patience. I also wish to express my appreciation to the members of the United Synagogue Commission on Jewish Education and its Committee on Textbook Publication, especially to Mr. Barnet Cohen, Rabbi George Ende, Rabbi Hyman Chanover, Rabbi Josiah Derby, Mr. Henry R. Goldberg, Dr. Morris S. Goodblatt and Dr. Solomon Grayzel, Dr. Leon S. Lang; to the readers, Mrs. Midge Decter, Miss Sarah Fuchs, Mrs. Jennie J. Honor, Mr. Jacob Julius, Mr. Maurice Plotnick; and the teachers who tested the stories in class, Mrs. Rose Friedman, Miss Pearl Martin, Miss Eleanore Rivlin; to all who took time out of their busy days to help me make this a better book. I am especially indebted to Miss Emily Solis-Cohen, Miss Deborah Pessin, Mrs. Leah Gelb, and my sister, Mrs. Frieda Granatstein, for their careful and critical reading of the manuscript and their many constructive suggestions; and to my little niece, Helen Louise Victor, who was the first to hear these stories. My special thanks are due Mr. Peter Oldenburg, the designer of this book, and Lili Cassel, the artist. Miss Cassel's beautiful illustrations are more than adornment to the book. They are an integral part of it. Above all, I am indebted to my husband. He has opened doors for me into many worlds, including the world of Jewish lore. In all my writing his help and his encouragement have been my mainstay.

S.R.W.

"We cannot all be Moses, Isaiahs, Elijahs, but we dare not forget that we are in the tradition."

"Why Israel Survived" by Solomon Goldman, in the United Synagogue *Sabbath and Festival Prayer Book.*

Dear Parents:

This volume of Jewish hero stories is the first in a series, planned to introduce your child to the great personalities who created and moulded our Jewish tradition. The joyful celebration of Sabbaths and festivals at home and in school gave your child his first experiences in Jewish living. In providing these experiences, you played a central role. Your role can be equally important in the adventure your child is now entering upon, meeting for the first time his people's heroes, learning through identification with them what it means to be a Jew.

We hope that you will cooperate with the school in providing the equipment, music, visual aids and materials for handiwork and dramatic play that will bring the classroom work to life, and that the interest created in school will be carried forward and deepened in the home. The United Synagogue Commission on Jewish Education has spared no effort to make this a book that your child will want to keep and turn to again and again. Read the stories to him at home after they have been presented in class. If, at first, he is not ready to read the text by himself—and he may not be, since a seven-year-old's comprehension of language is often in advance of his reading skill— let him "read you the pictures." A guide for parents, in addition to one for teachers, is in preparation.

A few points of clarification may be needed. The series is planned to include heroes from all periods of our history. This first volume begins with Abraham and concludes with King Solomon. We have tried to tell the stories simply and directly, retaining as far as possible the spirit and language of the Bible. Where the Bible gives no account of a hero's childhood, as in the story of Abraham, traditional legendary material was drawn upon. Where the Biblical account is complete, only an occasional legend is used. But throughout the book Midrash has influenced the emphases and the point of view.

Many more stories were prepared than could be included. Since the school can count on having the child for only a limited period, a textbook must of necessity be selective. But you, the parents, have your child every day in the week, and can add to and enrich the contents of this book. It is my hope that supplementary stories, Biblical and Midrashic, about these same heroes, will soon be made available for your use.

May this little book awaken an interest in your child which will lead him to the great sources of which these stories offer only a foretaste.

S.R.W.

Contents

The Story of King Solomon

United Synagogue Commission on Jewish Education

Elias Charry
CHAIRMAN

Josiah Derby
VICE-CHAIRMAN

Louis L. Ruffman
SECRETARY

Hyman Chanover
Azriel Eisenberg
George Ende
Sylvia C. Ettenberg
Henry R. Goldberg
A. Hillel Henkin
Leo L. Honor
Ario S. Hyams

Harold Kastle
Alter F. Landesman
Harry Malin
Stanley Rabinowitz
Zevi Scharfstein
Simon Shoop
Abraham Simon
Samuel Sussman

Judah Goldin, *Dean, Teachers Institute, Jewish Theological Seminary*

Simon Greenberg, *Executive Director, United Synagogue of America*

Wolfe Kelman, *Executive Secretary, Rabbinical Assembly of America*

Abraham E. Millgram, *Educational Director, United Synagogue of America*

Committee on Textbook Publication

Henry R. Goldberg, Chairman
Barnet Cohen
Josiah Derby
Morris S. Goodblatt
Solomon Grayzel

Leo L. Honor
Leon Lang
Isidore S. Meyer
Abraham E. Millgram
Saul Teplitz

The Story of Abraham
and His Son Isaac

How Abraham Found God

Long, long ago, there lived a little boy named Abraham. Abraham's home was in a faraway land, in a city called Ur. There he lived with his father and mother and two younger brothers.

In those days cities had walls around them to keep enemies out. Every night the gate to the city was locked. Every morning the gate was opened. Abraham liked to watch the people pass in and out. Some rode on small donkeys. Some rode high on tall swaying camels. There were people on foot, shepherds, companies of soldiers.

Abraham asked questions about everything.

"Why do camels wear bells?

"Where do the merchants come from?

"Where are the shepherds going?"

One night Abraham was lying on the flat roof of his house, looking up at the stars. The twinkling stars made

him think of the new bracelets that twinkled on his mother's arms. That very day he had watched the goldsmith make them.

Suddenly a question came into his mind. "The goldsmith made my mother's bracelets. *But who made the stars?* Who made the heavens, the earth, the fields, the river? WHO MADE THE WORLD?"

It was the biggest, most important question that Abraham had ever thought of. He hurried down the ladder, into his house to ask his father.

In those days people had not yet come to know God. They prayed to the sun or the moon. They said the king was god. They bowed before idols, figures made of stone or metal or wood. Abraham's father, Terah, made idols and sold them in his shop. He was carving a little idol when Abraham came into the room. It looked like a tiny grinning man.

"Father," Abraham asked, "who made the world?"

Terah answered, "The gods made it," and he pointed to the idols standing in a row.

Then he gave Abraham the little idol he had just finished and said, "You may have this new god for your own, Abraham. He will protect you."

Abraham looked at the little figure in his hand.

"You are nice to play with," he said to it. "But I do not believe you are a god. You have eyes but you cannot see. You have ears but you cannot hear. You have a mouth but you cannot speak. My father just made you. So how could you have made the world?"

The next day Abraham went to see his uncle who was an important man, an officer of the king. Abraham found him near the tower in the center of the city.

"What brings you here, little nephew?" his uncle asked.

Abraham answered, "I am looking for the God who made heaven and earth."

"You have come to the right place," his uncle said. "King Nimrod is god. He built this tower that reaches to the skies. He made the heavens and the earth."

But Abraham shook his head. Once he had seen Nimrod's face and it was cruel. He could not believe that Nimrod was God.

So he set out again, this time to see another uncle who was a shepherd. It was evening when Abraham found him, tending his sheep outside the city walls.

"Peace, little nephew," the shepherd uncle greeted him. "What brings you here?"

Abraham answered, "I am looking for the God who made heaven and earth. Can you tell me where to find Him?"

"He is right above you in the heavens," his uncle said, pointing upward. "The moon is god."

Abraham looked up at the moon. It filled heaven and earth with its silver light.

"My uncle knows," Abraham thought. "The moon is god."

As he spoke a cloud covered the moon and the sky was darkened.

Abraham sighed. "The cloud is stronger than the moon for it has driven it from the sky. The cloud must be god."

But now a wind arose and scattered the clouds, and the heavens were filled with stars.

Abraham laughed. "How foolish of me to think that the cloud was god. The stars are gods."

For hours and hours Abraham lay on his back among the sheep, looking up at the twinkling stars. At last he fell asleep. When he awoke it was morning and the stars had faded from the sky. Abraham lifted his eyes to the sun. Then he closed them quickly for the light blinded him.

"Forgive me, mighty sun," he cried. "It is you who are god."

But now Abraham remembered that the sun would set at the close of day.

"The sun cannot be god," he said, "for in the evening it will set. The moon is not god. The stars are not gods. And surely the king is not god."

Suddenly Abraham understood. "There is someone above them all. He made heaven and earth and all that is in them."

Abraham had his answer at last.

Abraham
Breaks the Idols

For a while Abraham told no one what he had learned about God. Then one day, when he was alone in his father's shop, an old woman came in.

"I want to buy a god," she said, "a strong one."

"But you bought an idol yesterday," Abraham said to her.

20

"I did," the woman answered, "but thieves came in the night and stole it. I dare not stay in my house without a god to protect me."

Abraham said to her, "Is it not foolish to think that an idol that could not save itself, will save you?"

Then Abraham told her about the one true God.

"Only He can protect you," Abraham said.

So the woman left without buying the idol.

When she had gone, Abraham took a hatchet and began breaking the idols into bits. Smash! Crash! Down came the idols one after another until only the largest one was left. Abraham put the hatchet in its hand and set a plate of meat before it.

Terah, who had heard the noise, came rushing in.

"Abraham!" he cried. "What has happened? Who broke the idols?"

Abraham answered, "I came into the room with a plate of meat. All the little gods stretched out their hands and grabbed the meat before the big one could. This made the big one so angry, he took the hatchet in his hand and smashed all the little ones to bits. See, the hatchet is still in his hand."

Terah turned to Abraham in anger. "Am I a fool that you tell me this story? These idols are made of wood and stone. I myself have made them. Can they open their lips? Can they move? Can they walk? How then could the big god have smashed the little ones?"

Abraham answered, "How then could these gods help you, father? Make no more idols. Pray to the one God who made heaven and earth. He is the only God."

Terah looked about him anxiously. "Hush, Abraham," he said. "It is dangerous to talk this way. If King Nimrod hears of it, he will throw you into his fiery furnace. Oh, my son, why must you be different from everyone around you? Bow down before the idols as you used to do."

But Abraham refused. From that day he prayed only to God.

God's Promise

Years passed. Abraham grew to be a man and married his cousin Sarah. Sarah was as good as she was beautiful and loved God as he did. Together, they brought up their young nephew, Lot, whose father and mother had died. Abraham was a shepherd now. He had moved from Ur to Haran and tended his sheep and goats in the fields outside the city walls. Many families had joined him. They had put away their idols and prayed only to the one true God. But in the cities people still bowed down to idols and called the cruel king god.

And now something happened that was to change Abraham's whole life. One night as he walked alone under the stars, he heard God's voice calling him.

"Abraham, leave your country and your father's house, and go to a land that I will show you. I will make of you a great nation and I will bless you and make your name great. Through you all the nations of the earth will come to know Me."

So Abraham, with Sarah and Lot and all the families who had joined them, set out from Haran. Abraham rode at the head of the people. After him came camels carrying the women and children and the old people, little donkeys with loads bigger than they were, shepherds with their flocks and herds, young men with spears and bows and arrows.

Each night Abraham chose a place to camp. Then the camels knelt and the people climbed down. Tents were set up. Fires were made. In the morning they set out again. The hot sand burned their feet. The sun beat down on them. Desert winds blew stinging sand into

their faces. A river had to be crossed. On and on they traveled.

At last one day they came upon a wide and beautiful valley. Spread out before them were green pastures, streams of water, mountains in the distance. It was the land of Canaan. Abraham's heart filled with joy.

"How good is this land," he said. "Streams run down between the mountains. There are trees for shade, grass for the cattle, fields of barley and wheat for bread."

Then Abraham heard the voice of God, saying, "Abraham, I give this good land to you and your children and your children's children forever."

Joyfully Abraham called the people together, and they gave thanks to God.

So Abraham came to live in the land of Canaan. The people of Canaan called him "the Hebrew," which means "the man from the other side of the river."

In Abraham's Tent

The doors of Abraham's tent were always open. Travelers, poor people from the cities, all who needed a friend were welcomed.

Once an old white-haired man came to his tent. Abraham served him milk and cheese and the flat round cakes of bread that Sarah baked. After the man had eaten he thanked Abraham for his kindness.

Abraham said as he always did, "Do not thank me. It is God who gives us our food. Let us give thanks to God."

But the old man refused.

"Your God is not my god," he said. "I have a god of my own."

And he put his hand into the folds of his cloak and drew out a small wooden idol.

Angrily Abraham drove the man from his tent. The next moment he heard the voice of God speaking to him.

"Abraham, that man is ninety-nine years old. All these years I have been patient with him. I saw to it that he had food to eat and clothing to wear. And you could not be patient with him for one night."

Abraham bowed to the ground and said, "O God, forgive me. I have done wrong."

God answered, "Why do you speak to *Me?* Go and ask the old man to forgive you."

Quickly Abraham ran after the old man. He found him under a thorn bush, bent beneath his heavy load.

"Forgive me for sending you away," Abraham said to him. "Come back with me, I beg you." And he lifted the load from the old man's shoulders and put it on his own.

So they returned to the tent. Abraham piled sheepskins on the floor to make a soft bed for the old man, and covered him with his own blanket.

Never again did Abraham turn a stranger from his door. Travelers spoke of his kindness. Some of them said, "It is his God who teaches him to be our friend." And they put away their idols and prayed only to the God of Abraham.

Abraham
Rescues Lot

Wherever one looked, sheep and lambs, cattle and kids and goats grazed. Some belonged to Abraham and some to his nephew, Lot. Their flocks and herds had grown so large, it was hard to find grass enough for them all. The shepherds of Lot began quarreling with the shepherds of Abraham. One would say, "Take your sheep from this hill. We found the place first." The other would say "*We* found it first." And there would be angry words and blows.

One day Abraham sent for Lot and said to him, "There must be no quarrel between you and me and between my shepherds and your shepherds, for we are brothers. It is better that we separate."

Lot agreed, and they walked together to the top of a hill. The whole land of Canaan lay spread before them.

Abraham said to Lot, "Choose where you wish to go. If you go to the left, I will go to the right. If you go to the right, I will go to the left."

Far to the east Lot could see a wide green valley with the Jordan River running through it. It seemed to him like a garden, well watered everywhere.

"I choose the valley of the Jordan," Lot said. "I will journey eastward with my family, my flocks and herds."

So Lot and Abraham separated. Lot went down into the valley and settled near the city of Sodom, while Abraham moved slowly up into the hills to Hebron.

But Lot soon learned that the Jordan valley was not so pleasant a place to live in as he had expected. The kings of the cities were always fighting. If a king wanted gold or supplies of food he attacked a neighboring city, seized whatever he and his men could lay their hands on, and rode off with it.

One night a man came to Abraham, breathless with running.

"Lot, your nephew, has been captured!" he cried. "Four kings came from across the Jordan and attacked the cities of the plain. The king of Sodom escaped to the mountains. But Lot and his family, all his men and his belongings, have been carried off."

Quickly Abraham called out his faithful followers.

Before the sun rose they were on their way to rescue Lot, a few hundred men against the armies of four kings. All day they rode hard. By nightfall they had caught up with the enemy. Abraham divided his men into two companies, and they fell upon the kings' armies in the darkness and defeated them and drove them across the Jordan.

They found Lot and the rest of the people who had been captured, badly frightened but safe. The goods the kings had carried off, gold and weapons, clothing and food, lay in a heap on the ground. Abraham's men gathered it up. Then they rode back to Sodom, bringing with them Lot and the people and all the goods.

The king of Sodom came out to meet them. He saw the gold and weapons, the clothing and the food, and he said to Abraham, "Give me the people and keep the goods for yourself." For it was the custom that whatever was taken in battle went to the victors.

But Abraham had fought only to save his nephew Lot. He said to the king of Sodom, "I will take nothing that is yours, not even a thread or a shoelace."

Then he said goodbye to Lot and returned home.

Abraham
Pleads With God

Sodom, the city where Lot had come to live, was a wicked city. So was its neighboring city, Gomorrah. If a stranger came to either one of them, crowds surrounded him in the street. They mocked him and beat him and stole his belongings. If the stranger went to a judge to complain, the judge punished the stranger instead of the thieves.

God heard the cries of the strangers and decided at last to end the wickedness. But first he spoke to Abraham about it, for He wanted Abraham to understand His ways.

"Abraham," God said, "the sins of Sodom and Gomorrah are very great. The cities shall be destroyed."

Abraham's heart filled with pity.

"O God," he said, "It cannot be that *all* the people of Sodom are wicked. Suppose there are fifty good people in the city. Surely You will not destroy the good people together with the wicked ones. Shall not God, the Judge of all the earth, do right?"

God answered, "If I find fifty good people in Sodom I will spare the whole city for their sake."

Again Abraham spoke. "You are God and I am only a man. Yet I must speak to You. Suppose there are not quite fifty good people. Suppose there are only forty-five."

God said, "I will spare the city for the sake of the forty-five."

"What if forty good people are found there?" Abraham asked.

God promised to spare the city if there were forty good people in it, if there were only thirty, or even twenty.

But still Abraham pleaded. "O God, do not be angry with me. I will speak but once more. Suppose there are ten good people."

God said, "I will spare the city for the sake of the ten."

That evening two travelers arrived in Sodom. Lot, Abraham's nephew, was sitting at the gate of the city. He ran to meet the strangers and brought them to his home. There he set food before them and invited them to spend the night.

News of the arrival of the travelers spread through

33

the town. Soon an angry crowd surrounded Lot's house. All the people of Sodom were there, from the oldest to the youngest.

"Where are the men who came to you tonight?" they shouted. "Bring them out to us."

Lot stepped out and shut the door behind him.

"I beg you, my brothers," he said, "do not do this shameful thing."

But the men muttered angrily, "This fellow Lot came to live with us only a little while ago. Now he is trying to tell us how to behave."

"Move aside," they shouted, "or we will treat you worse than we treat them."

They would have seized Lot, but the strangers put out their hands, drew him into the house, and bolted the door.

Now the strangers were really angels in disguise. They said to Lot, "Take your wife and family and escape. Sodom is to be destroyed because of its wickedness."

Then they took Lot and his wife and two daughters by the hand and hurried them out of the city.

"Do not look back," they warned them. "Do not stay in the valley. Escape to the mountains lest you be destroyed."

Lot and his daughters hurried on and came to a place of safety. But Lot's wife could not bear to leave the city. As the sun rose, she looked back. Fiery salt was raining down from heaven. It covered the wicked cities and all the valley. It covered Lot's wife and she became a pillar of salt.

If ever you visit Israel, go down into the Jordan valley. There you will see a great sea of salt, the Dead Sea. Nothing can live in it, not even a fish. People say it is the place where Sodom and Gomorrah used to be, the cities that Abraham tried to save.

Isaac Is Born

Abraham was an old man now. He had menservants and maidservants, flocks and herds, donkeys and camels, silver and gold. He had followers who loved and honored him. But he had no son. And he wanted a son more than anything in the world.

One night God came to him in a dream and led him out under the sky.

"Look up," God said, "and count the stars, if you can."

Abraham looked up. The heavens were filled with stars, so many stars one could not possibly count them.

God said, "As many as the stars shall your children be, your children and your children's children after you."

Then Abraham knew that God meant to give him a
son.

One day at noon Abraham was sitting in the doorway
of his tent. The sun burned hot and he was glad to be
able to rest in the shade. Looking out over the hot sands
he saw three strangers coming toward him.

Abraham ran out of the tent door to meet the strangers, bowing before them to the ground. "Do not pass
by, I beg you. It is hot and you are tired. Rest under the
tree. I will fetch you water and a bit of food."

The strangers sat down under an oak tree whose
branches spread over the tent.

Abraham called his servants, and they took off the strangers' sandals and washed the hot dust from their feet, while Abraham hurried into Sarah's tent.

"Sarah, we have guests," he said. "Take a measure of our best flour and bake cakes."

Then he ran to the herd and fetched a tender calf and gave it to a servant to prepare. When the food was ready he set it before the strangers and stood near them under the trees while they ate.

After the meal, one of the strangers said to Abraham, "Where is Sarah, your wife?"

"She is in the tent," Abraham answered.

The stranger said, "I will come back at this time next year, and Sarah shall have a son."

Sarah heard the stranger, for she was standing in the tent door behind him. And she laughed to herself, saying, "How can anyone as old as I have children?"

The stranger heard her laugh and asked, "Is anything too hard for God? When this time comes round next year I shall return, and Sarah shall have a son."

And so it was. Before the year had passed Sarah bore a child. Again she laughed, this time for joy.

"Who would have thought I would give Abraham a son in his old age?"

And she named the baby Isaac which means laughter.

God Teaches Abraham and Tests Him

Abraham loved little Isaac.

When the baby no longer had to be nursed, Abraham made a feast in his honor. All the neighboring princes were invited.

Soon Isaac was following his father about in the pasture. He liked to see the new born lambs. The mother sheep licked them with her tongue. He liked to watch when a new well was dug. Often he stood beside his father on the hilltop near a flat rock called an altar. Abraham would kill a lamb or kid and burn it on the altar, watching the smoke rise up toward heaven. This was called an offering or a sacrifice. It was a way people had in those days of thanking God for His kindness.

There were some people in those far-off days who said it was not enough to sacrifice animals. They knew so little about God that they thought He wanted them to sacrifice their first born sons.

And now God said, "I shall let Abraham prove he
trusts in Me. He shall prove it in such a way that all men
will learn that I do not want the sacrifice of children."

At that moment Abraham heard the voice of God
calling, "Abraham."

"Here I am," Abraham answered.

God said to him, "Take your son, your only son,
Isaac, whom you love, and offer him up on Mount
Moriah."

Abraham's heart grew heavy with sorrow, for Isaac
was dearer to him than his own life. But he had always
obeyed God. So early in the morning he saddled his
donkey, and set out with Isaac for Mount Moriah. At the
foot of the mountain he took the bundle of wood for the
sacrifice and laid it on Isaac's back.

40

"Father," Isaac said, "we have fire and wood. But where is the lamb for the offering?"

Abraham answered, "God will provide a lamb, my son."

When they reached the mountain top, Abraham built an altar out of stones. Tears ran down his cheeks as he made ready for the sacrifice.

But suddenly a voice from heaven called, "Abraham, Abraham. Do not lay your hands upon the boy. Do nothing to him. Now I know that you trust in Me, for you were ready to give Me your son, your only son."

Looking up, Abraham saw a ram caught in the bushes by its horns. He offered up the ram instead of Isaac. Then, full of joy, Abraham took Isaac by the hand, and they returned home.

A Wife for Isaac

Years passed. Sarah had died and Abraham and Isaac missed her greatly. One day Abraham sent for Eliezer, his oldest servant whom he trusted with everything.

"Eliezer," Abraham said, "it is time Isaac married. Go to my family in Haran and choose a wife for him, a good wife like his mother Sarah."

"What if the maiden I find does not want to come with me?" Eliezer asked. "Shall I take Isaac back to the land you came from?"

"No, no!" Abraham cried. "Do not take my son out of this land. It is the land that God has given us."

The next morning Eliezer took ten camels, loaded them with rich gifts from his master's house, and set out for Abraham's old home.

It was evening when Eliezer reached the walls of Haran. He made his camels kneel down to rest. Then he looked up at the women, coming out of the city to draw water from the well.

"There are so many beautiful young women," Eliezer thought. "How shall I know which one to choose for Isaac's wife?"

And a plan came to him, "If I ask one of these maidens for a drink of water and she gives it to me and also offers to draw water for my camels, I shall know that she will be a good wife for Isaac."

Then he prayed to God to send such a maiden. He had hardly finished praying when a beautiful maiden came out through the city gate carrying a pitcher on her shoulder. She went down to the fountain, filled her pitcher with water, and came up again.

Eliezer ran to her and said, "Please, let me drink a little water from your pitcher."

"Drink, my lord," the girl said kindly, and she lowered her pitcher and gave Eliezer a drink.

Then she looked at the hot and tired camels kneeling near the wall and said, "I will also draw water for your camels."

She emptied her pitcher into the trough, then ran again and again to the well until she had drawn water enough for all the camels.

"Whose daughter are you?" Eliezer asked her. "Tell me, please, is there room in your father's house for us to spend the night?"

"There is room both for you and your camels," the

girl answered. "I am Rebekah, the daughter of Bethuel."

Then Eliezer knew that this was Abraham's own niece, and he cried joyfully, "Blessed be the Lord God, who has shown kindness to my master and led me to this young maiden."

He gave Rebekah gifts, a gold ring and bracelets, and told her that he had come from her uncle, Abraham. Rebekah ran home with the happy news.

Now Rebekah had an older brother named Laban. Laban hurried to welcome Eliezer.

"Come in, O blessed of the Lord," he said.

And he spread straw for the camels and set food before Eliezer and his men.

But Eliezer would not eat until he had told them his errand, how Abraham had sent him to find a wife for Isaac, and how he had met Rebekah.

"Tell me," he said, "whether you will let Rebekah go with me to be Isaac's wife."

Laban answered, "It is God who has brought this to pass."

Then they called in Rebekah and said to her, "Will you go with this man?"

Rebekah answered, "I will go."

So early the next morning the family blessed Rebekah and she set out with her maid servants and her old nurse to look after her.

On and on they traveled until one evening Rebekah looked up and saw a man walking in the fields.

"Who is that man?" she asked Eliezer.

"It is Isaac, my master's son," Eliezer answered.

At that moment Isaac looked up and saw Rebekah.

The camel knelt and Rebekah alighted and covered her face with her veil. Isaac welcomed her and led her into the tent that had belonged to his mother, Sarah.

So Rebekah became Isaac's wife. And he loved her.

The Story of Jacob

The Twins Who Were
Not Alike

There were twin babies in Rebekah's tent, two little sons, just born. Everyone asked questions about them.

"Twins!" cried the children of the camp. "Do they look alike?"

"Not a bit alike," Rebekah's old nurse answered. "One is red and hairy all over. They are calling him Esau. The other is white and smooth. His name is to be Jacob."

The grown folk wanted to know which of the babies came first. This was a very important matter, for the one who was born first would have the birthright. This meant that he would be head of the family some day, when his father died.

"Esau, the hairy one, came first," the nurse answered. "He is a few minutes older than his brother."

The older the twins grew the more different they became. Esau was a skillful hunter. He would go off to the fields and hills with his bow and arrows, and return with deer slung over his shoulder. He always took the best part of the meat, prepared it the way his father liked, and brought it to him in his tent. Esau was his father's favorite.

Jacob was a peaceful shepherd like Abraham and Isaac. Day and night he watched over the sheep. Often, as he looked up at the stars, he thought of the promise God had made to his grandfather, Abraham, and to Isaac, his father. *"Your children shall be as many as the stars. I will make of you a great nation. Through you all the nations of the earth shall be blessed."*

Jacob wished that he were the elder brother and had the birthright. Then *he* would be the leader of that great nation.

One day he was cooking a thick, red pea soup—pottage, it was called—when Esau came in from his hunting, tired and very hungry.

"Let me have some of that good red pottage," Esau begged him.

"I will trade it for your birthright," Jacob answered.

"What good will my birthright do me? I am starving," Esau said.

And he sold his birthright to Jacob for a dish of pottage. Then Jacob knew how little the birthright meant to Esau.

Which Son Shall Have the Blessing

Years passed and Isaac grew old and blind. He could seldom leave his tent. It was Jacob who looked after the family. He tended the fields and the flocks. He made the offerings to God.

Esau was interested only in his hunting. Once he came home bringing two Hittite women he had married. In those days a man could have more than one wife. Esau's wives brought idols with them and prayed to them. Isaac and Rebekah were very unhappy about this.

At last Isaac grew so weak he knew that he might die any day. The time had come to give his blessing to the son who was to take his place. Now Isaac meant the blessing to go to his eldest son, Esau. But Rebekah wanted Jacob to have it.

She said to Isaac, "Your father Abraham broke the idols in his father's house and came to this new land to serve God. But Esau lets his own wives pray to idols. How can I be happy if Esau is master here?"

Isaac answered, "Esau is the first-born. The blessing must go to the first-born. It has always been so."

A little later Rebekah heard Isaac say to Esau, "My son, take your bow and arrows and bring in a deer. Make me a good stew, the kind I like. It will strengthen me, so that I may sit up and bless you before I die."

Rebekah made up her mind that Jacob, not Esau, should get the blessing.

As soon as Esau had gone, she sent for Jacob and told him what she had heard.

"My son, do as I tell you," she said to him. "Go to the flock and fetch me two kids. I shall prepare the meat the way your father likes, and you shall take it to him. He will think that you are Esau and will give you the blessing of the first-born."

Jacob ran and fetched the kids as his mother had said, and Rebekah prepared a tasty stew. Then she covered

52

Jacob's smooth arms with the skins of the kids to make them feel hairy like Esau's. She put the dish of meat in his hands and sent him to his father's tent.

"Father," Jacob said.

"Who are you?" asked Isaac.

Jacob answered, "Esau, your first-born. Sit up and eat of the meat I have prepared, and bless me."

"Come closer and let me feel you, my son," Isaac said.

So Jacob went near and his father felt him.

"The voice is the voice of Jacob," Isaac said, "but the hands are the hands of Esau."

Then he kissed Jacob and gave him the blessing of the first-born.

No sooner had Jacob left his father's tent than Esau came back from the hunt. He, too, made a tasty stew and brought it to his father.

"Arise, father," he said, "and eat of your son's meat that you may bless me."

"Who are you?" Isaac asked.

Esau answered, "I am your son, your first-born, Esau."

"Then who was it who brought me the meat before? I ate it before you came, and blessed him."

When Esau heard the words of his father, he cried with a great and bitter cry, "Bless me, too, O my father."

But Isaac answered, "Your brother came and took away your blessing. I have made him master here, and blessed him with corn and with wine. What, then, shall I do for you, my son?"

Esau cried, "Have you only one blessing, father? Bless me also, O my father."

Then Isaac blessed Esau also, but with a different blessing. The blessing of the first-born had gone to Jacob.

The Ladder That
Reached to Heaven

Again Rebekah sent for Jacob. This time she begged
him to go to her old home in Haran. "Esau is threaten-
ing to kill you," she said. "Stay with my brother Laban

a little while until Esau gets over his anger. Then I will send for you."

So Jacob left his home and set out on the long journey to Haran. When night came he stopped in a lonely spot beside the road, laid a stone under his head for a pillow, and lay down to sleep.

And a dream came to him. In his dream he saw a ladder that reached from earth to heaven. Angels were going up and down the ladder. And a voice spoke to him. "I am the Lord, the God of Abraham and Isaac. I will guard you, Jacob, wherever you go and will bring you back to this land."

Then Jacob awoke. "Surely," he said, "God is in this place and I did not know it."

He took the stone that he had slept on, and set it up to show that this was a holy spot. And he named the place Bethel.

Jacob Works Fourteen Years for a Wife

Early in the morning Jacob set out again and came at last to the land of the east where his mother Rebekah had lived. In an open field he saw a well. Three shepherds and their flocks were gathered about it. Jacob went up to the men and spoke to them.

"My brothers, where do you come from?"

"From Haran," they answered.

"Do you know Laban, the grandson of Nahor?"

"We do," they said. "There is Rachel, his younger daughter, with her sheep." And they pointed to a lovely shepherd girl coming toward them.

Jacob ran to the well, rolled off the great stone that covered it, and drew water for Rachel's sheep. Then he told her that he was her cousin, Rebekah's son, and kissed her. Rachel hurried home to bring the news to her father.

So Jacob came to live with his uncle Laban and tended his sheep. A month passed and Laban said to Jacob, "You do not have to work for me without pay because you are my nephew. Tell me what your wages shall be."

Jacob, who had come to love Rachel dearly, said to Laban, "I will work for you seven years if you will give me Rachel as my wife."

Laban agreed. So Jacob worked for Laban seven years. But they seemed like a few days because of his love for Rachel.

When the seven years had passed, Jacob said to Laban, "Now give me my wife, as you promised."

Then Laban called all the people of the place together and made a wedding feast. In the evening he brought in the bride. She was covered with a heavy veil so that her face could not be seen. Jacob took her for his wife. But

in the morning, when the veil was lifted, he saw that the bride was not Rachel, but Leah, her older sister.

"What is this that you have done to me?" he cried to Laban. "I worked seven years for Rachel and you have given me Leah."

Laban answered, "In our country the younger daughter does not marry before the older. Wait one week. Then I will give you Rachel for a second wife. But you shall have to work for me seven years more."

So Jacob worked seven years more for Rachel, whom he loved.

Jacob Becomes Israel

When the fourteen years had passed Jacob said to Laban, "Now let me take my family and return to Canaan." For he longed for his father and mother and his own land. But Laban begged Jacob to stay on. So Jacob tended Laban's flocks for another six years, receiving sheep and goats for his work.

Leah had borne Jacob many sons and a daughter during these years. But Rachel had only one child, a son, Joseph. Joseph was the youngest of eleven brothers. At last, when Joseph was seven years old, Jacob set his wives and children on camels, took his cattle, his sheep and goats, and set out for his father's house in Canaan.

When they reached the Jordan River Jacob sent messengers ahead to find out how Esau felt toward him after all these years. The messengers returned saying, "Esau is on his way to meet you with four hundred men."

Then Jacob's heart was filled with fear.

"O God," he prayed, "save me from my brother Esau, for I fear he will kill me together with the mothers and children."

When he saw his brother coming, he approached him anxiously, bowing before him seven times. But Esau had

gotten over his anger. He ran to meet Jacob and threw his arms about him. The old quarrel was forgotten.

Now Jacob and his family moved on slowly through Canaan. At Bethel, where Jacob had dreamed of the ladder that reached to heaven, they stopped to give thanks to God.

Again Jacob heard God's voice. "Your name shall no longer be Jacob, but Israel. You shall be the father of a great nation. This land which I gave to Abraham and Isaac, I give to you and your children's children forever."

Once more Jacob and his family moved on. Near Bethlehem Rachel had a second child, a son, Benjamin. And there she died.

At last Jacob reached his father's house in Hebron. Rebekah had died in the years he was away. But Isaac was still alive.

Jacob set up his tents beside his father's, and took care of him for the rest of his days.

From that time Jacob was called Israel, which means Prince of God, and his children and children's children were called the Children of Israel.

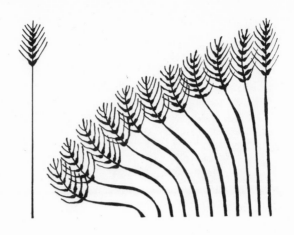

The Story of Joseph

The New Coat

Of all his sons, Jacob loved Joseph best. Joseph looked like his beautiful mother Rachel, who had died when he was seven years old. Whenever Jacob saw him, he thought of Rachel whom he had loved.

One day Jacob gave Joseph a beautiful coat of many colors. It was not a short shepherd coat. It was a long coat such as princes and chieftains wore. None of his brothers had one like it. Joseph put on his fine coat and ran off to the pasture where his brothers were tending the sheep. The brothers grew angry when they saw it.

"It is just as we thought," they murmured to one another. "Our father loves Joseph more than he loves us. He means to make him ruler over us."

From that day Joseph's brothers watched him jealously.

Harvest time came. All the family worked in the fields, cutting the ripe grain and binding it into bundles, or sheaves.

One morning Joseph said to his brothers, "Brothers, listen to this dream I had last night. We were all binding sheaves of grain, when my sheaf arose and stood upright and your sheaves came round and bowed down to my sheaf."

Joseph's brothers said to him, "Do you really think you are going to rule over us? Are we to bow down to you like the sheaves of grain?"

The next morning Joseph told them of another dream he had had. He said, "In my dream, the sun and moon and eleven stars bowed down to me."

This time his father scolded him. "What sort of dream is this that you have had? Shall I and your mother and brothers bow down before you to the ground?"

The brothers hated Joseph for having the dreams and for talking about them.

It happened, soon after this, that the brothers went off to feed their flocks near Schechem. When they had been gone for some time, Jacob sent Joseph to see whether all was well with them. Joseph set out from Hebron and found his brothers in a field, a long way from home. The brothers caught sight of him when he was still far off. He was wearing the coat of many colors. Their anger flared up when they saw it.

"Look," they cried. "The dreamer is coming! Let us kill him and we shall see what will become of his dreams."

But Reuben, the eldest, came to Joseph's help.

"Let us not take our brother's life," he begged. "See,

here is a pit." And he pointed to a deep hole that had once held water. "Throw him into the pit, but do not kill him."

Reuben thought that later, when his brothers were busy elsewhere, he would draw Joseph out of the pit and bring him back to their father.

The brothers tore off Joseph's coat, the coat of many colors, and threw him into the pit. Then Reuben went off by himself, but the other brothers sat down to have their meal. Looking up, they saw a company of Ishmaelites on their way to Egypt. Their camels were loaded with spices. Now Judah knew that merchants like these bought boys and girls to sell as servants in far-off lands.

He said to his brothers, "Why should we let Joseph die in the pit? He is our brother. Let us sell him to the Ishmaelites. They will carry him far away where he will never rule over us."

The brothers agreed. They drew Joseph out of the pit and sold him to the Ishmaelites. When Reuben returned, he hurried over to the pit. Joseph was not there.

"The boy is gone!" he cried to his brothers. "How can we go home to our father?"

Then the brothers took the coat of many colors, dipped it into the blood of a kid, and sent it to their father with a message. "We have found this coat. See whether it is your son's."

Jacob recognized the coat at once.

"It is my son's coat," he cried. "A wild beast has killed him. My Joseph has been torn by a wild beast!"

And Jacob mourned for his son many days. All his children tried to comfort him, but he would not be comforted.

Joseph Goes Down Into Egypt

Down into Egypt went the Ishmaelite merchants, taking Joseph with them. There they sold him to Potiphar, an Egyptian officer of Pharaoh, the king. How different Egypt was from Joseph's home in Canaan with its hilly pasture lands, its flocks and herds! The land of Egypt was flat, with a broad river flowing through it. There were crowded cities and great temples. In the temples the people worshipped images of animals that they

69

thought were gods, the bull, the crocodile, the cat. But Joseph prayed only to the God of Israel.

Whatever Joseph did turned out well, so that Potiphar was pleased with him and made him his most trusted servant. He put him in charge of everything, his house and his fields, all that he had.

But again trouble came to Joseph. The wife of his master grew angry at him though he had done no wrong, and told her husband stories about him which were not true. Potiphar believed his wife's stories and put Joseph into prison.

The keeper of the prison also came to like and trust Joseph and put him in charge of all the other prisoners. Among these were two important prisoners, the chief butler and the chief baker of Pharaoh, who had angered the king.

One morning, when Joseph was bringing the butler and the baker their food, he noticed that they looked worried.

"Why do you look so sad?" he asked them.

"We had dreams last night," the butler answered, "and there is no one to tell us their meaning."

"Tell the dreams to me," Joseph said. "Perhaps I can help you."

Then the butler said, "I dreamed I saw a vine with three bunches of ripe grapes. I squeezed the grapes into Pharaoh's cup and placed the cup in his hand."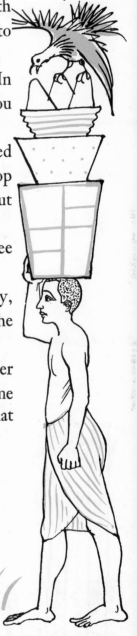

Joseph said, "This is the meaning of your dream. In three days Pharaoh will free you from prison and you shall serve him his cup of wine as you used to do."

Then the baker spoke. "I too had a dream. I dreamed that I was carrying three baskets on my head. The top basket was filled with all kinds of cakes for Pharaoh, but the birds were eating them."

Then Joseph said, "Yours is not a good dream. In three days you will die."

And so it was. In three days, on Pharaoh's birthday, the butler was freed from prison and sent back to the palace. But the baker was hanged.

Before the butler left, Joseph said to him, "Remember me, and speak of me to Pharaoh so that he may take me out of this prison. For I have done nothing wrong that they should keep me here."

But the butler forgot Joseph.

Pharaoh's Dream

Two years passed, and Joseph was still in prison. Then one night, Pharaoh had a dream. He dreamed that he was standing on the bank of the River Nile when seven fat cows came up out of the river and grazed on the shore. After them seven thin and ugly cows came up. Pharaoh had never seen such poor cows in all the land of Egypt. The seven lean cows swallowed up the seven fat cows. But the lean cows did not become fatter. Then Pharaoh awoke.

But soon he fell asleep and had a second dream. This time he saw seven full, plump ears of grain growing on one stalk. After them seven thin, dry ears sprang up. And the seven thin ears swallowed up the seven full ears.

When Pharaoh awoke in the morning he was greatly troubled. He sent for all his magicians and wise men, but no one could tell him what his dreams meant. Suddenly the chief butler remembered Joseph. He told the king about the dreams that he and the baker had had long ago in prison, and of the young man, a Hebrew, who had explained the meaning of their dreams.

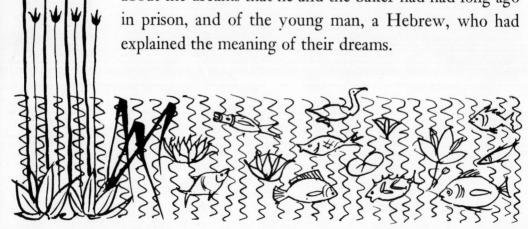

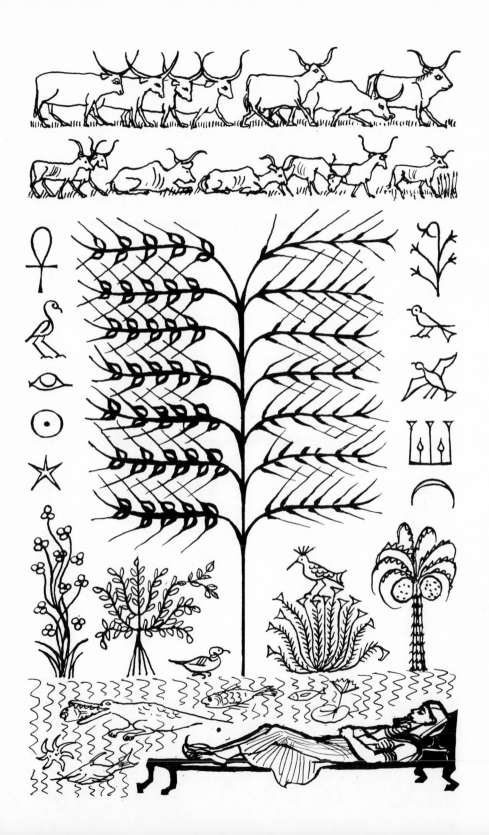

"All that the young man told us came true," the butler said. "I was brought back to the palace and the baker was hanged."

So Joseph was sent for. Quickly he was taken out of prison, bathed, dressed in fresh clothes and brought before the king.

Pharaoh looked down from his throne and said, "I have been told that you understand dreams and can tell their meaning."

Joseph answered, "It is not I. Only God can give Pharaoh a true answer."

Then Pharaoh told Joseph his dreams, the dream of the seven thin cows that swallowed up the fat cows and the dream of the thin ears of grain that swallowed up the full ears.

Joseph said, "The two dreams of Pharaoh are one. God has sent the dreams to warn you. The seven cows are seven years, and the seven ears of corn are seven years. Behold, seven years of plenty are coming to Egypt. There will be more food than one can measure. But after that there will be seven years of hunger when nothing will grow. The good years will be forgotten because of the bad years."

"What is there that we can do?" Pharaoh asked.

Joseph answered, "Find a wise man, one you can de-

pend on, and put him in charge of the land. Let him appoint officers to gather part of the grain during the good
years and store it in great storehouses. When the seven
bad years come and there is hunger in the land, you can
open up the storehouses and the people will have food."

Pharaoh said to Joseph, "There is none so wise as you.
You shall be in charge of my house. Whatever you say,
the people shall do. See, I set you over all the land of
Egypt."

Then Pharaoh took off his signet ring and put it on
Joseph's hand. He had Joseph dressed in fine linen and
made him ride in his royal chariot.

Up and down the land Joseph traveled, learning about
everything. The good years came and he gathered up the
corn and stored it in storehouses in the cities. There was
so much corn it could not be measured. It was piled up
in the storehouses like the sand beside the sea.

In these good years Joseph married, and two sons were
born to him. He named the first one Manasseh and the
second Ephraim.

The seven good years came to an end and the seven
bad years began just as Joseph had said. Nothing grew
in Egypt or in the lands roundabout. Joseph opened up
the storehouses and people came from everywhere to
buy corn.

The Brothers in Egypt

In the land of Canaan there was no food to be had.

Jacob said to his sons, "I have heard that there is corn in Egypt. Go down to Egypt and buy food so that we may not die."

One day Joseph looked down at the crowds of people who had come to buy corn. There among them he saw his own brothers, all of them except the youngest, Benjamin. Joseph knew his brothers at once, but they did not recognize him for he had been only a boy when they saw him last. They bowed before him with their faces to the ground, not knowing that the great Egyptian lord was their own brother, Joseph, whom they had sold as a slave.

Joseph pretended not to know them, for he wanted to see whether they had changed.

"Where do you come from?" he asked.

They answered, "From the land of Canaan to buy food."

"You are spies," Joseph said roughly.

"No, my lord, we are honest men, not spies. We are twelve brothers, all sons of one man in the land of Canaan."

"Twelve? Where, then, are the other two?" Joseph asked.

"The youngest is with our father," the brothers explained, "and the other one is gone."

"It is just as I said," Joseph insisted. "You are spies. But I will put you to a test. If you are honest men, let one of you stay here in the prison house. The rest of you go and carry food to your families. Then come back and bring your youngest brother with you. In this way your words will be proved. Do not return unless you bring your youngest brother with you."

Then Joseph had one of the brothers, Simeon, put into prison before their eyes.

The brothers spoke anxiously among themselves in Hebrew, not knowing that Joseph understood. "God is punishing us. We are guilty because of Joseph. He begged us to let him go, but we would not listen."

Joseph saw how sorry his brothers were for the wrong they had done, and he turned away from them and wept. Then he ordered his servants to give them corn, and to put the money they had paid into their sacks.

The brothers loaded their donkeys and set out. On the way home they stopped at an inn where Reuben opened his sack to get food for the donkeys.

"Brothers," he cried, "my money has been returned. See, it is in my sack."

The brothers turned toward one another, trembling.
Simeon had been imprisoned. Their money had been returned. What was the meaning of these strange things?

When the brothers reached home they told their father
all that had happened. "The lord of the land spoke
roughly to us," they said. "He put Simeon into prison
and told us not to come back unless we brought our
youngest brother with us."

Jacob cried out, "Why did you tell the man you had
a younger brother?"

"We could not help it," Judah answered. "The man
asked, 'Is your father alive? Have you another brother?'
How could we know he would say, 'Bring your brother
down to Egypt'?"

When the grain was eaten, Jacob said to his sons, "Go
down to Egypt again. Buy us a little food."

They answered, "We cannot. The lord of the land
warned us not to return unless we brought our youngest

brother with us. If you will let Benjamin go with us, we will go down and buy food. Otherwise we cannot go."

Jacob said, "No, no! Simeon is gone and now you want to take away Benjamin. Benjamin shall not go with you. His brother Joseph left me and never returned. Only Benjamin is left of Rachel's sons."

Then Judah spoke. "Father, send the boy in my care and let us set out at once so that we may live and not die, you and we, and our little ones. I swear that I will bring Benjamin back to you."

Jacob agreed at last.

"If it must be," he said, "prepare a present for the man, a little honey, spices, almonds. And take back the money you found in your sacks. There may have been a mistake. May God make the man merciful to you, so that you may bring back Benjamin, and Simeon also."

So the brothers took the present and the money they had found in their sacks and returned to Egypt, taking Benjamin with them.

I Am Joseph

When the brothers arrived in Egypt, they were taken at once to Joseph's house.

"You are to eat with our master this noon," the servant explained.

The brothers were frightened. "Why should the great lord of Egypt invite us to his house?" they wondered. "Can he be looking for an excuse to seize us and make us slaves?"

But the servant spoke to them kindly, and brought Simeon out of the prison house. Together the eleven brothers were led to Joseph. They bowed before him to the ground.

"Is your father well?" Joseph asked them. "The old man you spoke of—is he still alive?"

"Our father is alive and well," they answered.

Joseph pointed to Benjamin. "Is this your youngest brother of whom you spoke? God be good to you, my son."

Then he left the hall quickly, for he loved his brother Benjamin, and he could not keep back his tears. He went into his own room and wept. Then he washed his face and returned.

"Serve the meal," he said to the servants.

The brothers were surprised to find themselves seated according to age, from the oldest to the youngest. They looked at one another in wonder. How could the Egyptian have known each one's age?

When the dinner was over, Joseph called his servant aside and said, "Fill the men's sacks with food, and put every man's money in his sack as you did before. Then take my silver cup and put it in the sack of the youngest."

The servant did as Joseph had told him.

The next morning, the brothers set off on their donkeys. They had not gone far when they saw Joseph's head servant coming after them.

"My lord was good to you," he said. "Why have you taken his silver cup? It is a wicked thing that you have done."

"Why do you speak to us like this?" the brothers cried. "When we found money in our sacks we brought it back to you from Canaan. Why, then, would we steal silver or gold from your master's house? If you find that one of us has the cup, let him die."

Quickly the brothers lowered their sacks and opened them. The servant searched the sacks one after the other, and found the cup at last in Benjamin's sack. The brothers cried aloud in grief. They reloaded their donkeys and returned to the city.

When they came to Joseph, they bowed before him to the ground.

"What shall we say to you, my lord?" they cried. "How can we prove that we are innocent? Behold, we are your slaves."

Joseph answered, "Only the man in whose sack the cup was found shall be my slave. As for the rest of you, go in peace to your father."

Then Judah drew near to Joseph and pleaded with him. "O my lord, I beg you, listen to me and do not be angry with me. Benjamin is a child born to our father in his old age. Our father loves him. The boy's mother bore him two sons. One of them went away and never returned. If harm comes to this one also our father will die of sorrow. I beg you, let *me* be your slave instead of the boy. Let Benjamin go back to his father."

Then Joseph could no longer control himself. He sent his Egyptian servants out of the room.

"I am Joseph," he cried out. "Tell me about our father."

The brothers could not answer for fear and amazement.

"Come near me, I beg you," Joseph said to them. "Do you not see that I am really your brother Joseph? Do not be angry at yourselves because you sold me into Egypt. It was not you who sent me here but God. He sent me

ahead of you to save many lives. Go and tell our father."

Then Joseph put his arms about Benjamin and kissed
him. After this he kissed all his brothers.

While they talked together messengers came from
Pharaoh saying, "Tell your brothers to go and fetch
their father and their families. Give them wagons to bring
their wives and little ones. The best of all the land of
Egypt shall be theirs."

So the brothers returned to their father in Canaan.

"Father, father, Joseph is still alive," they cried. "He is ruler over all the land of Egypt."

Jacob could not believe them.

They had to repeat the words that Joseph had said to them and show him the wagons that Joseph had sent. Then at last he believed. His heart filled with joy.

"Joseph, my son, is still alive," Jacob said. "I will go and see him before I die."

So Jacob and his sons and daughters, his grandchildren and great-grandchildren went down into Egypt. Joseph hurried to meet his father. Then he brought him his sons, Ephraim and Manasseh.

"I did not expect to see even you," Jacob said to Joseph, "and God has let me see your children also."

And he placed his hands on the boys' heads and blessed them, saying, "May the God of my fathers Abraham and Isaac, the God who has taken care of me all my life, bless these lads. May they become a great people and be called by my name, 'Children of Israel'."

So Jacob and all his family came to live in the land of Egypt. Pharaoh gave them the rich pasturelands of Goshen, and they settled there with their flocks and herds. And Joseph took care of his father all the rest of his days.

The Story of Moses

The Baby Who Was Kept a Secret

Years and years passed. Jacob and Joseph and all the brothers had died. But their grandchildren and great grandchildren stayed on in Egypt. Their numbers grew greater and greater.

Then a new Pharaoh came to the throne of Egypt, a proud and cruel king.

"I am the greatest king that ever ruled," he said. "All men are my servants."

And the Egyptians bowed before him until their faces touched the ground.

"Pharaoh is god," they said.

The new Pharaoh saw the children of Israel, free men, tending their flocks in Goshen, and he said, "The Israelites are too numerous and too strong. They shall be my servants. I will put them to work building cities in which to store our war supplies. The hard work will weaken them."

The oldest of Pharaoh's wisemen said timidly. "O Pharaoh, the Israelites belong to the family of Joseph.

Do you not remember Joseph who saved Egypt in the time of the great hunger?"

But Pharaoh would not listen.

The Children of Israel were taken from their flocks and herds. All day long they worked in the brickyards and the fields, mixing clay with straw, baking the bricks in hot ovens, raising the walls of the new cities higher and higher. Taskmasters stood over them. If an Israelite rested for a moment, if he raised a hand to wipe the sweat from his forehead, lash-sh-sh, down on his back came the taskmaster's whip. Many Hebrew slaves died at their work. But more and more babies were born, so that there were as many Israelites as ever.

Then Pharaoh thought of a cruel and terrible plan. He sent messengers up and down the land, commanding that every Hebrew baby boy that was born be thrown into the river.

"Soon there will be no more Hebrews left," he said.

In a little hut not far from the palace, a Hebrew baby boy had just been born. He lay in the arms of his mother, Jochebed. His sister, Miriam, looked down at him.

"O Mother," Miriam said, "what shall we do? We cannot let our baby be drowned in the river."

Her mother comforted her. "We will keep the baby hidden and you, Miriam, will help me."'

For three months Miriam watched over her little

brother while her mother worked in the fields. As he grew older, it became hard to keep him quiet. One day she had just gotten the baby to sleep when an officer of Pharaoh rode by their door. Miriam watched anxiously until he was out of sight. Then she hurried to the baby.

"O little brother," she whispered, "you fell asleep just in time. If the soldier had heard you crying, you might be in the river now."

That night the family decided it was no longer safe to keep the baby with them. "We must entrust him to God's care," Jochebed said.

She went down to the river and cut an armful of the long reeds that grew along the bank. These she wove into a little basket-boat. Miriam helped her fill the cracks inside and out with tar so that no water might get through. In the morning Jochebed laid the baby gently in the basket and set it down in the river among the rushes. Miriam hid among the tall reeds on the river bank to keep watch. The water of the river rocked the basket gently to and fro.

Suddenly there were sounds of laughter and merry voices. Pharaoh's daughter was coming down from the palace to bathe in the river. Miriam saw the princess point to the little basket floating among the bulrushes. One of her maidens waded in and fetched it for her. The princess looked inside.

"A baby!" she cried. "It must be one of the Hebrew children."

Miriam's heart stood still. Would the princess turn the baby over to the soldiers? But Pharaoh's daughter was kind and gentle.

"Poor baby," Miriam heard her say, "no wonder you are crying. I will keep you. You shall be my own child. I shall call you Moses."

Then Miriam ran up to the princess and bowed, and said to her, "The baby is hungry, O Princess. Shall I fetch one of the Hebrew women to nurse him for you?"

"Go, fetch one," said the princess.

So Miriam ran home and returned quickly with her mother.

"Take this child and nurse him for me," the princess said. "When he is old enough you are to bring him to me in the palace."

Joyfully Jochebed carried her baby home.

So little Moses was saved. His own mother was to take care of him.

The Baby and the Crown

When Moses no longer had to be nursed, the princess sent for him and he came to live in the palace. He was a beautiful baby. Even the stern and cruel Pharaoh smiled when he saw him.

One day, the princess was sitting beside her father with little Moses in her arms, when a sunbeam stole down between the pillars of the great hall and fell on Pharaoh's crown. The sparkling jewels caught the baby's eye. He reached out his hands, took the crown from Pharaoh's head and placed it on his own.

Pharaoh's face grew dark with anger.

"What is this evil thing the child has done?" he asked. "What is its meaning?"

One of his wise men answered, "O Pharaoh, its meaning is clear. This child seeks your crown. As long as he lives Pharaoh's kingdom will not be safe. Let the child be put to death at once."

The princess held little Moses closer.

Then a second wise man spoke.

"If it seem good to you, O Pharaoh, let a test be made. Have two trays placed before the child, one filled with fiery coals and one with jewels. If the child grasps the jewels it will be a sign that he seeks your crown, and should be slain. If he grasps the coals we shall know that what he did was in childish play. In that case his life shall be spared."

The king agreed to the test. The two trays were brought in. Again the sparkle of the jewels caught little Moses' eye and he reached out to grasp them. But God sent an angel to push his hands aside and place them in the hot coals. The coals burnt the child's fingers. Quickly he put his fingers to his mouth, burning his tongue. Because of this Moses could not speak as clearly as others when he grew older. But his life was saved.

Moses Remembers His People

Moses grew up in the palace, wearing fine clothes, playing with the little princes in the palace gardens. Pharaoh's daughter told him stories about the gods the Egyptians prayed to. One of these gods looked like a cat, one like a crocodile, another like a bull. But often, as he grew older, Moses slipped through the garden down to the river where his real mother waited for him. And his mother told him stories about the God of Israel, and about his people, the Children of Israel.

"Long, long ago," she said, "the Hebrews were free men in the land of Canaan. A day will come when we shall be freed from slavery and return to that land. God has promised it. Do not forget that you are a Hebrew, little son."

94

Moses never forgot.

In time Moses was sent to school with the Egyptian princes. There he learned all that the wise men of Egypt could teach him. He grew up a fine, handsome young prince, and could have lived happily in the palace for the rest of his days. But he remembered his brothers, the Hebrew slaves. One day he went out to them where they worked in the fields and brickyards. His heart filled with pity as he saw them bowed down and groaning under their heavy loads.

Off in a field an old man stumbled and fell. The taskmaster lifted his long lash. Down it came again and again on the poor slave's back. The man cried out in pain. Full of pity and anger, Moses turned on the taskmaster and struck him down. The Egyptian lay dead at his feet.

The next day Moses went out into the field again. This time he saw two Hebrews fighting. Moses said to one of the Hebrews, "Why do you strike your neighbor?"

The man answered, "Who made you a prince and a judge over us? Do you mean to kill me as you killed the Egyptian?"

Then Moses knew that the thing he had done was known and that he must leave Egypt at once.

So he fled to the land of Midian.

Moses Finds a Wife

Evening was coming on when Moses stopped to rest near a well. As he sat there seven shepherd girls came down to draw water for their flocks. They had filled the trough and were leading their sheep to drink, when a band of rough shepherds came up, pushed the girls aside and led their own sheep to the water. Moses rose up and drove the cowardly shepherds away. Then he helped the girls water their sheep.

Now the seven girls were sisters, daughters of a priest of Midian, named Jethro. When they came home their father asked them how it happened they had returned so early, for the shepherds had been delaying them every day.

They answered, "An Egyptian came to our help and drove off the shepherds. He also drew water for us and watered the flocks."

"Where is the man now?" their father asked. "Go and invite him to eat with us."

Then Zipporah, the eldest of the sisters, ran back to the well and brought Moses home with her.

Moses stayed on with Jethro and became his shepherd. He married Zipporah, and two sons were born to them. Moses named his first son Gershom, which means stranger, for he said, "I was a stranger." He named his second son, Eleazar which means, "God is my help."

The Burning Bush

Never was there a shepherd more faithful or gentle than Moses. Once a kid escaped from the flock. Through thorns and brambles Moses followed it and caught up with it at last near a stream.

"Poor little one," Moses said. "I did not know you were so thirsty." He lifted the kid gently to his shoulders and carried it back.

Then God said, "Moses has pity on the sheep and goats of his flock. I will make him shepherd of My flock, the Children of Israel."

In all these years Moses never forgot his brothers in Egypt. He was thinking of them one day as he tended the sheep in the wilderness near Mount Horeb. Looking up, he saw a bush that burned with fire but did not burn up.

Moses drew near to see the strange sight, when a voice called to him out of the burning bush, "Moses, Moses!"

"Here I am," Moses answered.

The voice said, "Take off your shoes. The ground you are standing on is holy."

Trembling, Moses removed his shoes, bowed low, and covered his face with his hands.

The voice went on.

"I am the God of your fathers, the God of Abraham, Isaac and Jacob. I have heard the cry of My people in Egypt. I know their sorrows. The time has come to save them. Go to Pharaoh and tell him to let My people go."

But Moses said, "O God, who am I that I should go to Pharaoh? He will not listen to me, nor will the Children of Israel listen. They will not believe You have sent me."

God answered, "I will be with you and I will give you all the help you need."

Still Moses pleaded.

"You know that I do not speak well. I stammer."

Then God said, "Aaron, your brother, speaks well. He is on his way now to meet you. Tell him what to say and he will speak for you."

Moses said no more. He returned to his home and bade his father-in-law, Jethro, good-bye. Then he set his wife and his two small sons on a donkey and set forth.

On the way he met Aaron, his brother, coming to meet him as God had said. Together they went down to the land of Egypt.

Let My People Go

In the great hall of the palace Pharaoh sat on his golden throne. Soldiers guarded him. Priests and wisemen waited for his commands. Each guard held a long sharp spear. Each wiseman carried a magician's rod.

Moses and Aaron entered and stood before the throne, carrying nothing but their shepherd staffs.

"The Lord God of Israel has sent us to you, O Pharaoh," they said. "He says to you, 'Let My people go.'"

Pharaoh looked scornfully at the two Hebrews.

"Who is this Lord that I should listen to him? I do not know the Lord, and I will not let Israel go."

The Egyptian priests joined in mocking them. "If the Lord is indeed a God show us a sign or a wonder."

But God had prepared Moses and he knew what he must do. He threw his staff upon the ground. The staff changed into a serpent.

Pharaoh's magicians laughed and turned their own rods into serpents. But the next minute they turned pale, for Moses' serpent glided along the floor and swallowed up all the other serpents. Moses picked his serpent up by the tail, and it became a rod again.

The Egyptians, watching him, trembled.

"What is the meaning of this thing?" they wondered.
"Can it be a sign that the God of the Hebrews will prove
stronger than Pharaoh?"

Only Pharaoh was unafraid. He turned to Moses in
anger.

"Be gone!" he said, "Let us hear no more of this God of yours. You turn your people's thoughts from their work. Heavier work must be given them. Then they will have no time to listen to your words."

That same day Pharaoh sent orders to the taskmasters.

"Give the Hebrews no more straw to mix with the clay. Let them go into the fields and find straw for themselves. But make sure they turn in as many bricks each day as they did when we gave them the straw."

Now the Hebrew slaves had to work harder than ever. When Moses came out to them in the fields, they cried, "Who told you to go to Pharaoh? You have made things worse for us instead of better. Pharaoh will kill us with hard labor."

In his sorrow Moses prayed to God. "Lord, why did You send me here? For since I came to Pharaoh only trouble has come to my people."

God answered. "Pharaoh is cruel and stubborn. But I shall make such things happen in Egypt that he will know I am the Lord."

The next morning all the waters in the land of Egypt turned red as blood. For seven days the Egyptians had no water to drink.

After this, frogs came up out of the river, great swarms of frogs. They hopped into the palace, they hopped into Pharaoh's bedroom, into his bed. They hopped into the houses of his servants, into the ovens, into the bowls where the bread was kneaded.

Pharaoh sent for Moses and pleaded, "Pray to your God to take away the frogs. I will let your people go."

Moses prayed and God answered his prayer. But when

Pharaoh saw that the frogs were gone he would not let the Children of Israel go.

So new troubles came upon Egypt, plague after plague, swarms of lice, swarms of flies, sickness among the cattle, boils on the people, a hail storm that broke down all the barley and the flax, locusts that settled on the fields eating every green thing in their way, wild beasts, darkness in mid-day.

Again and again Pharaoh cried to Moses, "I have done wrong. Pray to your God to take away the plague and I will let the Children of Israel go."

Again and again Moses prayed, and God took away the plague. But each time Pharaoh broke his word. He did not let the Children of Israel go.

Then at last God said to Moses, "Tonight I will send one last plague upon Egypt. This time Pharaoh will surely let you go. At midnight I will take the Children of Israel out of Egypt."

The First Pesah

It was evening of the fourteenth day of the month of Nisan. In Goshen the Israelites were getting ready for a long journey. Hurriedly they gathered their belongings. There was no time to bake bread, but the women took the dough they had mixed in the wooden kneading bowls and packed it into their bundles. Each father sacrificed a lamb and roasted it in the fire. The family ate it with bitter herbs, standing up, ready to leave at any moment.

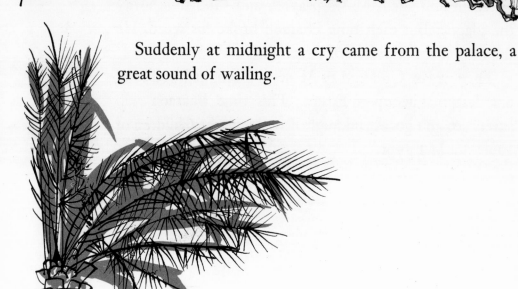

Suddenly at midnight a cry came from the palace, a great sound of wailing.

"What is it?" the little children of the Israelites asked.

The mothers answered solemnly, "The prince, Pharaoh's first born son, has died. Death has come to the first born son in every Egyptian house."

"Will it come to our house?" the children asked anxiously.

"No," said the mothers. "God has been merciful to us. Death has passed over the houses of the Israelites."

Soon messengers were knocking on every door.

"Set out at once. Pharaoh has sent for Moses and begged him to take us out. He fears the Lord our God."

So the Children of Israel left Egypt where they had been slaves for many years. There were thousands of them, mothers with babies in their arms, little children holding to their mothers' skirts, men with kneading bowls and household goods bound on their backs. There were cattle, and flocks and herds. The line stretched on and on.

When daylight came, the Israelites stopped in the wilderness to rest. There was no bread for them to eat, but the dough was still in the wooden kneading bowls. It had not risen and was without salt, but the women rolled it into thin, flat cakes and baked it in the hot sun. This was the first *Matzah*.

Then Moses called the people together and said to them, "When this time comes round each spring make a feast unto the Lord, you and your children and your children's children forever. It shall be the Festival of Passover. Eat no leavened bread for seven days, only *matzah*, unleavened bread. When your children ask you, 'Why is this night different from all other nights?' say to them, 'On this night God brought us out of Egypt, from slavery to freedom, from sorrow to joy.' "

At the Red Sea

No sooner had the Children of Israel left Egypt than Pharaoh changed his mind again.

"What is this that we have done?" he said, as he looked at the empty brickyards. "Why did I let our slaves go free? Who will make my bricks for me? Who will build my cities?"

He turned to one of the captains. "Where are the Israelites now?"

"They are camping near the Red Sea," answered the captain.

Pharaoh commanded, "Make the chariots ready, six hundred of them. Take our swiftest horses. I will overtake the Israelites and bring them back."

So the Egyptians set out, Pharaoh and his captains riding swiftly in chariots, horsemen and footmen, the whole army of Egypt. The Children of Israel, camping near the Red Sea, raised their eyes and saw in the distance Pharaoh coming after them. Before them was the sea, behind them the Egyptians. In their fright, the Israelites cried out against Moses, "Why have you brought us here to die in the wilderness?"

Moses answered quietly. "Do not fear. God will surely save you."

As he spoke, a cloud came down and hid the camp of Israel from the Egyptians.

Then Moses lifted his rod and stretched his hand out over the sea. And God sent a strong east wind. All night the wind blew. It raised the waters into two walls, leaving a dry path between. The Children of Israel passed through the sea on the dry path.

Now the Egyptians came riding up. Into the sea they went, after the Israelites. But the wheels of their chariots came off. The chariots dragged and overturned.

"Let us go back!" the Egyptians cried. "Let us flee from the Israelites. The Lord is fighting for them."

It was too late. As the last Israelite reached the other side Moses stretched out his rod. The waters returned and covered the chariots, the horsemen, all the army of Pharaoh. Not one of them was left.

Then Moses and all the people sang a song of thanks to God.

"Who is like unto Thee, O Lord?
Who is like unto Thee, glorious and holy,
Doing wonders!"

Miriam, Moses's sister, took a tambourine in her hands and the women went out after her dancing and rejoicing.

Bread From the Lord

Day after day the Israelites traveled in the desert. Wherever they looked they saw nothing but sand and rocks. No trees, no grass, no water! And the hot sun beat down upon them. Then, suddenly, waving palms appeared. Before them was a cool and grassy place with twelve springs of water and seventy palm trees. There they set up their camp. The children played in the shade of the trees. The boys climbed nimbly up the straight trunks and came down with bunches of plump, sweet dates.

"Are we to stay here?" the children asked. But the mothers said, "Moses is leading us to a mountain where we shall worship God. Then he will take us to the land of Canaan. It will be more beautiful than this, a land of hills and valleys and running streams."

Again the Israelites went out into the wilderness. And

now it became hard to find food. The people forgot the slavery they had suffered in Egypt. They remembered only the food they had eaten there. They complained to Moses, "In Egypt we had cucumbers and melons and onions. We had pots full of meat and all the bread we could eat. You have brought us into the wilderness to starve us."

But Moses was patient with the people. He prayed to God for them, and again and again God came to their help.

Once when they had no water to drink, God told Moses to strike a rock with his staff. Moses struck the rock and water gushed out, enough for the people and all the cattle.

Once when the people longed for meat, flocks of brown birds called quail flew over the camp. They flew so low the Israelites could catch them with their hands. That night pots of meat were cooking on all the camp fires.

One morning, the Children of Israel awoke to find the ground covered with small white flakes like frost.

"What is it?" the people asked.

Moses answered, "It is manna, bread that God has given you. Gather a measure of it for each one, but do not save any for tomorrow. Tomorrow God will send you more."

The people gathered the manna and ate it. It tasted like thin cakes made with honey.

There were a few people who said, "How can we be sure we shall have more manna tomorrow?"

These gathered an extra measure and hid it. The next morning more manna lay on the ground just as Moses had said. But the manna that had been hidden was full of worms.

When the sixth day of the week came, Moses said, "Today you must gather a double measure of manna. Save half of it for tomorrow, for tomorrow is the holy Sabbath and you must rest."

Again a few of the people disobeyed Moses. They said, "Why should we gather an extra measure? It will only spoil."

But this time the manna that had been saved stayed fresh and sweet, and no new manna lay on the ground.

From this time the Children of Israel were never without food. Day after day, through all the years in the wilderness, God sent them manna to eat.

God Speaks to the Children of Israel

The mountain of the Lord! The mountain of the Lord!"

Men pointed excitedly to a mountain in the distance. Its top was hidden in a cloud of smoke. It was Mount Sinai, the mountain to which Moses had been leading the Children of Israel for many weeks.

In a valley at the foot of the mountain, the Israelites set up camp and put their sheep out to pasture. While they were at work Moses went up the mountain side. His face was shining when he came down again.

"In three days the Lord will speak to you from the mountain top," he told the people. "All of you, men, women, children, shall hear God's voice."

Then Moses told them what they were to do.

"Make ready. Wash your clothes. Bathe in the stream. But do not go near the mountain until you hear the *Shofar* sound."

On the morning of the third day, the sound of a *Shofar* woke the people from their sleep. It was thundering and lightning. Moses led the people out of the camp and they stood at the foot of Mount Sinai. The mountain

115

was wrapped in smoke. The smoke rose up from it like smoke out of a furnace. The whole mountain quaked.

Louder and louder grew the sound of the *Shofar*. Louder and louder grew the thunder peals. Suddenly a voice spoke from the mountain top.

116

"I am the Lord thy God."

A hush fell upon the earth. Not a bird called, not a cow lowed. No creature stirred while God spoke to the Children of Israel at Mount Sinai.

117

I am the Lord thy God who brought thee out of the land of Egypt, out of the house of bondage.

Thou shalt have no other god beside Me.

Thou shalt not take the name of the Lord, thy God, in vain.

Remember the Sabbath day to keep it holy. Six days thou shalt labor and do all thy work, but the seventh day is a Sabbath in honor of the Lord thy God. On it thou shalt do no work, neither thou, nor thy son, nor thy daughter, nor thy servants, nor thy animals, nor the stranger within thy gate.

Honor thy father and thy mother.

Thou shalt not murder.

Thou shalt not commit adultery.

Thou shalt not steal.

Thou shalt not bear false witness against thy neighbor.

Thou shalt not covet.

These Ten Commandments God gave the children of Israel at Mount Sinai. And the people answered gladly, "Whatever God commands, we will do and obey."

The Golden Calf

It was several days after the Children of Israel had heard God's voice at Mount Sinai that Moses said to the people, "God has called me to the mountain top. I shall bring down the Ten Commandments engraved on tablets of stone. Wait for me until I return." Then he went up the mountain and disappeared among the clouds.

Days and weeks went by and Moses did not return. The people grew worried and frightened. They spoke. anxiously to one another as they tended their sheep. "What has become of Moses? Suppose he never comes back? Who will lead us out of this dreadful wilderness?"

The God who had spoken to them from the mountain top seemed far away. They longed for a god that they could see and touch, the kind of god they had known in Egypt.

When forty days and nights had passed, the people gathered in crowds around Aaron.

"Moses is gone," they said. "We do not know what has become of him. Make us a god to lead us, one that we can see, a god such as we knew in Egypt."

"If I do not do as the people say they will return to Egypt," Aaron thought. "I must keep them here until Moses returns."

"Bring me your earrings," he said to the people, hoping they would be unwilling to give up their jewels. But soon the men returned and tossed a heap of golden earrings at his feet. Slowly Aaron gathered up the earrings and melted them into a lump. Slowly he began carving out a calf with his tools. He kept his eyes toward the mountain, hoping each moment that Moses would return. But Moses did not appear and the calf was finished at last. A great shout went up in the camp. The people offered sacrifices to the golden calf and feasted and danced around it.

Suddenly the singing and the dancing stopped. Stand-

ing on the mountain side the people saw Moses, his eyes
blazing with anger. Two stone tablets were in his hands.
He flung the tablets with the Ten Commandments to the
ground and broke them into bits. Then he strode into the
camp, took hold of the golden calf, burnt it with fire and
ground it into dust.

"Aaron," he cried, "why did you make the people a
golden calf? How could you let them break God's com-
mandment?"

Aaron told Moses all that had happened, while the people listened, frightened and ashamed. Moses' anger was
gone now. He loved his people more than he loved his
own life.

"O God," he prayed, "forgive the people. Let me
teach them Your ways."

God said to Moses, "Come up the mountain again. I
will give you new tablets like the ones that were broken."

So Moses went up the mountain again and brought
down new tablets engraved with the Ten Commandments.

Patiently, day after day, Moses taught the people
God's law, the Ten Commandments engraved in stone,
and other laws God had taught him on the mountain
top. As long as he lived, Moses taught the Children of
Israel to love God and to keep His commandments.

A Tabernacle

In the camp of the Israelites hammers clanged, spindles whirred. The Children of Israel were building a Tabernacle, a great tent in which to keep the tablets of God's Law. To the Tabernacle they would bring their offerings. There they would come to pray and give thanks to God.

"Bezalel, the artist, will be in charge of the work," Moses had said. "Bezalel is wise and skilled. He will teach you to carve wood, to work in gold and silver and brass,

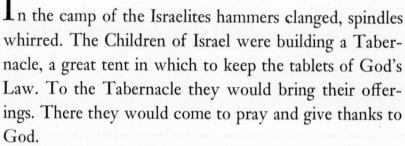

for the Ark of God

to set precious stones, to engrave and embroider. Whoever wishes may help him."

All the people wanted to help. They hurried to Moses, bringing gold and jewels, brass, wood, spices, oils, linen, goat's hair, ram skins, anything they had that could be used for the work. Moses had to send word through the camp, "Let no more offerings be brought. We have all that we need and more."

So the work began. Men cut down the trees that grew

in the mountains and planed them into poles to make the frame for the great tent. Tanners scraped skins into strong coverings for the roof and sides. Brass workers bent over hot fires, forming sockets and hooks and rungs. Women wove curtains of linen and goat's hair. Dyers dipped the skins and curtains into kettles of boiling dye, red and blue and purple.

Bezalel worked skillfully with gold and jewels. He made a beautiful Ark for the Tablets of the Law. It was covered inside and outside with gold. He made a golden altar and a golden lamp with seven branches. The light in the lamp would burn day and night. He made a breastplate for Aaron, set with twelve precious stones, one for each of the tribes. For Aaron and his sons were to be the *Kohanim*, the priests.

The Tabernacle was finished at last. Moses blessed the workers.

Joyfully, the people gathered in the outer court. Moses put the tablets of God's law, the stone tablets he had brought down from Mount Sinai, into the Ark. And Aaron and his sons carried the Ark into the Tabernacle.

The Children of Israel carried the Tabernacle with them on all their journeys. Slowly they moved on toward the Promised Land.

Forty Years in the Wilderness

More than a year had passed since the Children of
Israel had left Egypt. They were tired of wandering,
tired of the yellow sand and bare rocks, tired even of
the manna.

At last one day Moses pointed to the distant hills. "We
are near Canaan," he said, "the good land God promised to our fathers. Choose a man from each tribe to go
up and spy it out."

Quickly twelve men were chosen. They stood before
Moses, waiting for their orders.

"Start in the south, the Negev," Moses said. "Then
go up into the mountains. See what the land is like,
whether the soil is rich or poor, whether the people live
in strong cities or in villages, whether they are few or
many. Try to bring back some of the fruit of the land."

So the twelve men set out. After forty days they returned. A shout of joy went up in the camp, for the
men had brought with them fresh and juicy fruit, pome-
granites, figs, a cluster of grapes that was so large two

men had to carry it between them on a pole. Crowds followed the men to Moses' tent to hear the report.

"The land is indeed a good land, full of milk and honey," the leader said. "But we shall never be able to take it. It has walled cities and the people are like giants. We felt like grasshoppers next to them."

Two of the men, Caleb and Joshua, interrupted.

"We, too, went up into the land. It is a good land and we are well able to take it. Do not be afraid of the people of Canaan. God will help us."

But no one listened to Caleb and Joshua. The people were murmuring and weeping.

"It would have been better if we had stayed in Egypt!" someone cried. "Our wives and our little ones will be killed."

"Let us appoint a captain and go back to Egypt," another shouted.

"To Egypt! Back to Egypt!" The cry ran through the camp.

Suddenly the voice of Moses was heard above the shouts. His voice was stern but full of sadness.

"The Lord has spoken to me. You are not ready to go up into the land He promised. You have been slaves too long. Slavery has made you timid and afraid. For forty years you shall wander in the wilderness. Here your

children will grow up, brave and free. Your children, not you, shall enter the Promised Land."

So the Israelites lived on in the wilderness for forty years. They went from place to place, wherever they could find grass for their goats and sheep. The old people who had been slaves in Egypt died. The children grew up strong and brave.

Moses Leaves His People

The forty years of wandering had come to an end. Soon the Children of Israel would enter the Promised Land. But Moses knew that he would not go with them. He was an old, old man, and the time had come for him to die. For the last time he called the Israelites together.

"I am a hundred and twenty years old," he said to them. "I can no longer lead you. And God has called me to the mountain top. From Mount Nebo I shall look upon the Promised Land but I shall not enter it. But do not fear, for Joshua will be your leader."

Then Moses placed his hands on Joshua's head and said to him, "Be strong and of good courage. The Lord will be with you." And he gave Joshua a scroll on which he had written down all the laws that God had given him.

Turning to the people, Moses said, "Hear, O Israel, the Lord your God, the Lord is one. Love the Lord your God with all your heart and with all your soul and with all your might."

The people followed Moses out of the camp, and across the wide plains of Moab. At the foot of the mountain Moses said to them, "Turn back, my children. From here I must go on alone."

He climbed up into the mountain and disappeared in the heights.

Stories of the Judges

JOSHUA

DEBORAH

GIDEON

SAMSON

Into
the Promised Land

Joshua was now the leader of the Israelites. He looked across the Jordan River and saw a strong city blocking the way into the Promised Land. The walls around the city were so strong and wide that houses were built on top of them. It was the city of Jericho. Joshua sent two men to spy it out.

The men slipped into Jericho toward evening and went to the inn of a woman named Rahab. Rahab guessed who the strangers were but she kept their secret, for she knew that God would soon give the land to the Children of Israel.

The next afternoon soldiers of the king knocked at Rahab's door.

"Bring out the men who came here yesterday," the soldiers ordered. "They are Israelites come to spy out our land."

But Rahab had taken the men up to the roof and hidden them under stalks of flax.

She said to the soldiers, "The men are no longer here.

133

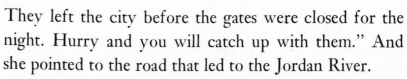

They left the city before the gates were closed for the night. Hurry and you will catch up with them." And she pointed to the road that led to the Jordan River.

Away went the soldiers out of the city and down the main road.

When it grew dark Rahab went up to the men on the roof. "Escape to the hills," she said. "Hide there until the soldiers give up the search."

Then Rahab tied a rope to a window and let the men slide to the ground outside the city, for her house was built on the city wall.

Before the Israelites left, they made Rahab a solemn promise that she and all her family would be spared when the city was taken. They gave her a red cord to tie to her window so that Joshua might know which house was hers.

When the spies returned to Joshua they reported. "The land can be taken. The courage of the people is melting away."

Now at last the Israelites crossed the Jordan River into the Promised Land. The Levites led the way, carrying the Ark of the Lord.

But the city of Jericho still blocked Joshua's way. Day and night the gates of Jericho were locked tight. No one was allowed to go in or out for fear of the Israelites. One dark night Joshua stole up to the city walls to examine

them more closely. Suddenly he saw a man with a drawn sword standing before him.

"Are you for us or for our enemies?" Joshua asked.

The man answered, "I have come to tell you how the city can be taken. The Lord has sent me."

Then he told Joshua what he was to do.

The next morning, the watchmen on the walls of Jericho saw a strange sight. A long procession was moving out of the camp of the Israelites. Seven priests, blowing rams' horns, carried the Ark of the Lord. Before them and behind them marched the soldiers of Israel. Without speaking a word, without a shout, the Israelites marched once around the city walls, then went back to their camp.

The next day the Israelites returned, and the next, and the next. Each day the people of Jericho grew more anxious and fearful. The seventh day came, and now the Israelites circled the city not once but seven times. Around and around they marched, silent as before.

Suddenly a command was heard, "Shout, for the Lord has given you the city."

A tremendous shout went up from the thousands of Israelites. The walls of Jericho crumbled and Joshua and his men rushed in.

The promise to Rahab was not forgotten. A red cord hung high up in the window of a house on the wall. The house was spared and Rahab and her family were taken safely to the Israelite camp.

On Joshua marched, up into the hills, through the valleys and along the sea coast, taking city after city. Sometimes the people of a city came out and asked Joshua to make peace with them. Often there was hard fighting. But Canaan was taken at last, and the land was divided among the twelve tribes.

The Story of Deborah

The Children of Israel were now farmers in the land of Canaan.

But they had always been shepherds. Farming was new to them. Now, the Canaanites, the new neighbors of the Israelites, believed that there were many gods, a god for the shepherds in the wilderness, a god for the farmers, a different god for each land, each valley and hilltop. They came to the Israelites and said, "Do you want your seed to grow? Do you want good crops? Then do as we do. Go up to the hilltop and bring a sacrifice to our god Baal. *Your* God is the God of the desert. He cannot help you here."

There were Israelites who believed the Canaanites and went up with them to the high places. There they made offerings to Baal and danced wildly around Baal's altars. More and more of the Children of Israel began praying to Baal.

The old men who remembered Joshua shook their heads. "Israel is forgetting God and His commandments," they said.

But new leaders arose to bring the people back to God's teachings.

In a green and beautiful valley spread out between the mountains, Israelite farmers tended their olive trees and their vineyards, their fields of barley and wheat. Often, looking up from their work, they saw long lines of camels moving slowly along the highway carrying goods from far off lands, cloth and pottery, ivory and spices.

But one day, instead of merchants, a great army marched into the valley, swift riders with horses and iron chariots, thousands and thousands of foot solders. Sisera, the captain of the Canaanite king, had come to conquer the Israelites. The soldiers overran the countryside. They attacked the farmers, seized their arms and carried off the armor makers.

Year after year Sisera stayed on. The farmers went on planting their seed and tending their vines. But the wine and the olive oil, the barley and the wheat went to Sisera and his men. Not a man in Israel dared to rise up against him.

But up in the hills lived a brave woman, a mother in Israel, named Deborah. People called her Deborah the Prophetess. Each day Deborah sat under a palm tree near her home, while people came to her from all parts of the land. She settled their disputes. She listened to their troubles. She taught them to trust in God.

Deborah saw that the faces of the children were pinched with hunger.

"How long shall we feed Sisera's army while our children go hungry?" Deborah said. "Let us arise and drive the Canaanites from our land."

The men lifted their hands helplessly.

"There isn't one spear among forty thousand of us," they said. "And every man of Sisera is armed. He has nine hundred iron chariots."

Deborah answered, "If God is with us nine *thousand* chariots will not save Sisera."

Then Deborah sent for a brave captain named Barak. "God has called you, Barak," she said. "Arise! Gather an army and march up to Mount Tabor. God will put Sisera into your power."

Barak answered, "If you will go with me, Deborah, I will go. But if you will not go with me, I will not go." For Barak knew that only Deborah could put courage into the people.

"I will go with you," Deborah said.

A call went out to the tribes. Ten thousand men of Israel answered the call. They came from Ephraim, from Benjamin, from Issachar, from Zebulon. Barak and Deborah led them to the top of Mount Tabor.

Down in the valley near the River Kishon they could see Sisera preparing for battle. His soldiers and chariots and horses, filled the plain. Suddenly the heavens grew dark. Rain poured down. The waters of the River Kishon began to rise.

"To the attack!" Deborah called to Barak. "See, the very heavens are fighting for us. This is the day when God will put Sisera into your power."

Barak gave the signal and the Israelites rushed down the mountain side and fell upon the enemy. They fought bravely, fearlessly. Sisera's army tried to flee before them, but the chariots stuck in the mud and overturned. The horses plunged in fright, trampling the riders underfoot. The River Kishon swept them away.

Then Deborah sang a song of thanks.

> Bless, O my soul, the power of the Lord.
> Those who love Thee shall be as the sun,
> Rising up, and going forth in his splendor.

The Midianites
Are Coming

For forty years there was peace in the land. Then once more trouble came to Israel.

On a farm in the peaceful valley, there lived an Israelite boy named Gideon. One day Gideon was helping his father with the barley harvest, when his sharp eyes caught sight of something moving in the distance.

"Father, look," he said. "Strange men are coming, on camels, great numbers of them."

His father shaded his eyes with his hand.

"They are Midianites," he cried. "They have come to carry off our crops. Run, Gideon. Take your grandfather and the women up into the hills. I must hide the cattle and the grain."

On came the Midianites, fierce men from the desert. Hoops of gold hung from their ears. Golden chains hung around their camels' necks. They set up their tents in the valley, trampled over the fields, stole and killed. Then back they went across the River Jordan, carrying with them the farmer's crops and cattle and sheep.

Year after year at harvest time the Midianites returned.

The Israelites grew poorer and poorer. They made hide-outs for themselves in caves, and threshed their grain in hidden places. So seven years passed by.

Gideon was now the only son left in his family. His brothers had been working peacefully in their fields, when two Midianite chiefs rode by and struck them down. Gideon was thinking of this one day as he beat out some grain among the rocks. Looking up, he saw a stranger sitting under an oak tree.

"The Lord is with you, brave warrior," the stranger said.

Gideon answered. "If the Lord is with us why has all this trouble come to us?"

The stranger said, "Go and save Israel from the Midianites."

Gideon looked at the man wonderingly.

"Who am I to save Israel? My family is the weakest in my tribe, and I am the youngest in my father's family."

The stranger insisted, "The Lord is sending you. He will be with you and you shall drive the Midianites out of the land."

That night Gideon tore down the altar of Baal that stood on the hilltop. When the people of the village awoke in the morning and saw what had happened they hurried to Gideon's house.

"Bring Gideon out," they shouted. "He must die for he has torn down Baal's altar."

But Gideon's father said to them, "Why do you take Baal's part and fight for him? If he is a god let him fight for himself."

The people turned to one another. "He is right," they said. "Let Baal fight for himself. We have turned away from the God of Israel. It is for this that trouble has come to us."

For the Lord and Gideon

The Midianites are coming!"

Watchmen hurried to Gideon with the news. He put his ram's horn to his lips and sounded the alarm. The men of the village gathered about him. Messages were sent to the tribes round about. "Come in the name of the Lord to drive the Midianites out of our land."

A great army of farmers answered the call. But Gideon noticed, as he walked among the men, that many looked with fear toward the Midianite camp.

"The Midianites have more men than can be counted," they whispered to one another. "Their camels are as many as the sands by the sea."

Then Gideon stood on a high rock and spoke to his men. "There are too many of you. With God's help a few can win against the many. Let anyone among you who is afraid go back to his home."

145

Many thousands of the men turned back. Ten thousand were left.

"There are still too many," Gideon said.

Then he put the men to a test. Not far away a spring of cool water flowed out of a cave, the spring of Ein Harod. Gideon led his hot and thirsty men past this spring. Many ran from their line and knelt down to drink. Others scooped up a handful of water and lapped it up with their tongues as they went on.

Those who left their lines and knelt down were sent home. Only three hundred men were left. Gideon said, "With these three hundred will God save Israel."

That night Gideon divided his three hundred men into three companies. To each man he gave a ram's horn and a pitcher with a lighted torch inside.

"Watch me carefully," he said. "Whatever you see me do, you must do. When I blow my horn let each one of you blow his horn and shout, "For the Lord and Gideon.""

In the blackness of the night the three hundred crept quietly down the hill and surrounded the camp of the enemy. Each one held a ram's horn in his right hand and the torch and the pitcher in his left hand. The Midianites were fast asleep in their tents.

Suddenly Gideon blew a great blast on his horn. Then he smashed his pitcher and waved his flaming torch. At once all the three hundred blew their rams' horns, smashed their pitchers and waved their torches shouting, "For the Lord and Gideon."

The Midianites awoke. Torches were flaring all around them. Trumpets were blowing. They heard the shouting and the crashing and thought that hundreds of companies had come against them. Full of terror, they struck one another in the darkness thinking that they were striking the enemy. Then they fled out of the camp screaming wildly as they ran.

Gideon and his men went after them. Down the valley the Midianites fled, across the Jordan river, away into the desert. They never came back.

Now all the people of Israel gathered around Gideon. "Be our king, Gideon," they shouted. "Rule over us, for you have saved us from the Midianites."

But Gideon said to them. "I will not rule over you, nor shall my sons rule over you. Only God shall rule over you."

Then Gideon returned to his farm.

So Israel was saved from the Midianites and lived in peace for many years.

The Story of Samson

There was another enemy, the Philistines, who troubled the Children of Israel. The Philistines lived in walled cities along the coast and came up again and again to attack the Israelites.

"Oh, that a hero might arise, a hero like Joshua or Gideon to save us from the Philistines," the people prayed.

Now there was a certain man of the tribe of Dan whose wife had no child.

One day a stranger appeared before her and said, "A son is to be born to you. He will take the lead in saving Israel from the Philistines."

Full of joy the woman told her husband what had happened. "I did not ask the man his name or where he came from," she said. "His face looked to me like the face of an angel."

The next day the stranger returned. This time the woman called her husband.

"If a son is born to us, how are we to raise him?" the husband asked.

The stranger answered, "Never cut his hair and let

him drink no wine. Raise him to serve the Lord from his birth to the day of his death."

In time the woman bore a son as the stranger had said. She named him Samson. No wine passed his lips. His hair was not cut. It grew thick and long, golden as the sun.

Soon neighbors saw that Samson had tremendous strength. Once when a lion came roaring at him, he seized the beast and tore him apart with his bare hands. Another time, when the Philistines locked him inside their city walls, he arose in the night, pulled up the great gate of the city, and carried it off on his shoulders, posts and all.

So Samson grew up and became the champion of the Israelites. The Philistines were in terror of him.

But trouble came to Samson. He fell in love first with one Philistine woman, then with another.

His father and mother said to him, "Is there no girl among your own people that you must go and get a wife from the Philistines?"

Samson would not listen to them.

The name of the second Philistine woman was Delilah.

The Philistine princes came to Delilah and said, "Coax Samson to tell you the secret of his strength. If you find out how we can take him captive, each of us will give you eleven hundred pieces of silver."

That night Delilah said to Samson, "Tell me the secret of your strength. How can you be made helpless?"

Samson answered, "If I were bound with seven new bowstrings I would become as weak as any other man."

When Samson lay asleep Delilah bound him with seven new bowstrings. Then she called, "Samson, the Philistines are coming!"

Samson sprang up and snapped the bowstrings as easily as if they had been burnt with fire.

Then Delilah said, "You mocked me and told me lies. Now tell me truly how you can be bound fast."

This time Samson said, "If I were bound with ropes that had never been used, I should lose my strength and be like other men."

So Delilah took new ropes and bound him. Then she cried, "The Philistines are coming, Samson."

Samson snapped the ropes from his arms like thread.

"You have lied to me again," Delilah cried. "Tell me truly the secret of your strength."

Samson pointed to the loom on which Delilah ha'd been weaving and said to her, "If you were to weave my seven locks of hair into your loom and fasten them in with a pin, I should grow as weak as any other man."

The next night, while Samson slept, Delilah took his seven locks of hair and wove them into her loom. Again she called, "The Philistines are upon you, Samson."

Samson awoke and pulled up the loom.

Then Delilah wept and said, "How can you say you love me, when you do not trust me? Three times you have fooled me."

Day after day she begged and coaxed and cried until Samson grew tired of it all, and told her his secret. "God set me apart to serve Him, and commanded me never to cut off my hair. If my hair were cut off I should lose my strength and be like any other man."

This time Delilah knew that Samson had told her the truth. She sent for the Philistine princes and they came bringing with them the money they had promised her. Delilah hid the Philistines in the next room. Then she put Samson to sleep with his head on her knees. While he slept she had someone creep in softly and cut off his hair.

Again Delilah called, "The Philistines are upon you, Samson!"

Samson awoke and lifted his great arms to shake himself free. They were as weak as those of any other man. The Philistines seized him and put out both his eyes. Then they brought him to the prison house in Gaza. There they bound him with brass chains and made him walk round and round, turning the mill stones that ground their grain.

A day came when the Philistine princes held a great celebration in the temple of their god, Dagon.

"Come," they said. "Let us make a sacrifice to our god, for he has delivered Samson into our power."

In the midst of the merrymaking Samson was brought out of the prison house to amuse the people. A little boy led Samson by the hand, blind and helpless. Thousands of the Philistines went up on the roof of the temple to see him better. Samson could hear them laugh and jeer at him. His heart was bitter against the Philistines because of his blinded eyes.

"Let me lean against the pillars of the temple," he said to the boy who was leading him. The boy placed him between the pillars that held up the building.

Then Samson prayed, "O Lord God, give me my strength! Just this one time."

He grasped the two great pillars, one with his right hand, the other with his left.

"Let me die together with the Philistines," he said.

Then he pulled with all his might. The building fell in on all the princes and all the people that were in it. So thousands of the Philistines died and with them Samson.

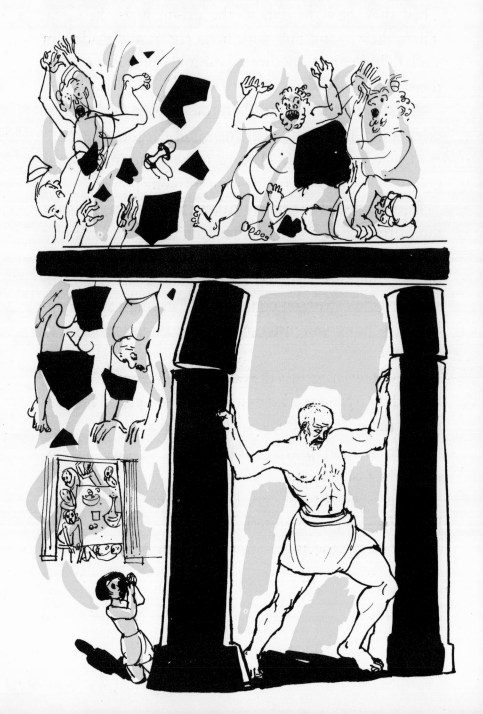

The Story of Samuel, Saul and David

The Child Samuel

Have you wondered where the Ark of God was kept now that the Children of Israel lived in Canaan? It was in a little temple in the town of Shiloh. The good priest Eli, a great, great grandson of Aaron, looked after it.

Families would go up to Shiloh on festivals, fathers and mothers with their children. After the sacrifice there would be a feast for them all. Among those who came up every year was a farmer named Elkanah and his wife, Hannah.

Now Hannah had no child, and she wanted a child more than anything in the world. When she saw the many mothers with their children, she wept and could not eat.

Her husband said to her, "Hannah, why is your heart so sad? Am I not dearer to you than ten sons?"

Hannah was too unhappy to answer. She arose and went inside the temple and stood before the Ark.

"O Lord," she prayed, "look upon my sorrow, and remember me. Let me have a son and I will surely bring him to the temple to serve You all the days of his life."

God heard Hannah's prayer and a son was born to her. She named him Samuel which means "The Lord heard my prayer." As soon as Samuel grew old enough to do without his mother, Hannah brought him to Eli.

"Here is the child for whom I prayed," she said to him. "I have brought him to you to serve in the temple. As long as he lives, he shall serve the Lord."

Then Hannah kissed her little son and left him with the kind and gentle old Eli. She and Elkanah went back to the farm, but each year they returned. Hannah always brought Samuel a new coat that she had made for him.

One year when Hannah came, she found Samuel wearing a little priest's robe like Eli's. Eli had given it to him because Samuel was now helping him with his work. Each day Samuel rubbed the lamp over the altar until it gleamed, and filled it with fresh olive oil so that the light might never go out. At night he slept in the temple, where he could be near Eli and run to him when he called. For Eli had grown old and blind.

One night as Samuel lay asleep, he heard a voice calling, "Samuel, Samuel!"

"Here I am," he said and ran to Eli, for he thought it was Eli who had called him.

"I did not call you," Eli said. "Go back to sleep."

So Samuel went back, but again he heard the voice.

"Samuel, Samuel!"

Again he arose and went to Eli. "Here I am," he said, "for you called me."

"I did not call, my son," Eli said again. "Go back to sleep."

Samuel did as he was told. A third time he heard the call and arose and went to Eli. Then Eli knew that God was calling the lad, and he said to him, "Lie down once more, my child, and if you hear the call again say, 'Speak Lord, for Thy servant hears.' "

So Samuel went back to his place and lay down, and again the voice called, "Samuel, Samuel!"

Samuel said, "Speak, for Thy servant hears."

Then God spoke to Samuel and told him many things that were to happen in the days to come and what he was to do.

When Samuel grew up he became a judge and a leader in Israel. He went from town to town, up and down the land, teaching the Children of Israel to love God and obey Him. People called him a prophet.

Give Us a King

When Samuel grew old, the elders of the people came to him and said, "Give us a king to rule over us. All nations have kings."

Samuel was greatly surprised and troubled. "God is our King," he said. "We need no other."

But the people would not listen to him.

Then Samuel said, "If you have a king this is what he will do. He will take your sons to be his soldiers and to plow his fields and to make his swords and spears. He will take your daughters to be his cooks and bakers. He will take the best of your fields and vineyards and a tenth of your sheep. And you will be his servants."

But the people insisted, "Give us a king so that we may be like other nations."

Then God said to Samuel, "Listen to the voice of the people. I will send you a young man from the tribe of Benjamin. Anoint him king over Israel. He shall save them from the power of the Philistines."

Now there was a farmer in Benjamin who had a son named Saul, a young and handsome man. There was no handsomer man in all of Israel. He was head and shoulders taller than any other Israelite. It happened one day that the farmer's donkeys wandered away. Saul took one of the servants and set out to search for them. They wandered for three days without finding them.

Then Saul said, "Let us go back or my father will stop worrying about the donkeys and worry about me."

But the servant said, "There is a prophet who lives in this town. Perhaps he can help us."

So they went up to the city gates and there they met an old man coming toward them. It was Samuel on his way to the hilltop to make a sacrifice. The moment Samuel saw Saul he knew that this was the young man sent by God.

He said to Saul, "I have been expecting you. Do not be anxious about your father's donkeys. They have already been found."

Then he invited Saul to join in the sacrifice saying, "The place of honor has been reserved for you."

Saul answered in surprise, "Am I not one of the tribe of Benjamin, the smallest tribe in Israel? And is not my family the least important in the tribe? Why do you honor me in this way?"

Samuel made no answer. He took Saul with him to the feast, and Saul ate, and spent the night with him. Early

the next morning Samuel awakened Saul and walked
with him to the end of the city.

"Tell your servant to go ahead," he said.

When the two were alone, Samuel took a horn of oil
and poured it over Saul's head. And he kissed him and
said, "God has chosen you to be king over Israel."

When Saul returned home, he told no one what had
happened between him and Samuel.

Saul Saves a City

A month went by.

In the city of Jabesh-Gilead the people were in great trouble. Jabesh-Gilead was an Israelite city on the other side of the Jordan River. Their Ammonite neighbors, fierce fighters, had come with a great army and surrounded the city walls. No one could come in or go out.

When the food was gone and the water was gone the elders of the city said to the Ammonites, "Make peace with us and we will be your servants."

But the king of Ammon answered, "I will make peace with you on one condition, that I put out the right eye of every man among you. So shall all Israel be disgraced."

Then the Israelites of Jabesh-Gilead said, "Give us seven days. If help does not come to us in seven days, we shall give ourselves up and you may do with us as you please."

The Ammonites agreed to wait. Messengers were sent from Jabesh-Gilead to all the towns of Israel.

One afternoon Saul came home from his plowing and found the people gathered in crowds, weeping and talking excitedly.

"What has happened?" he asked.

"Messengers have come from our brothers in Jabesh-Gilead," someone answered. And he told Saul how the king of Ammon had demanded the right eye of every man in Jabesh-Gilead.

Saul's anger blazed. He took the two oxen with which he had been plowing, killed them and cut them into pieces. Then he sent the pieces to all the tribes of Israel with the message, "Come out with Saul to save our brothers in Jabesh-Gilead. If you do not come, this will be done to your oxen."

Every man in Israel answered the call. They came by the thousands.

Then Saul said to the messengers from Jabesh-Gilead, "Go back to your city and tell the people they will be saved by midday tomorrow."

That night Saul set out at the head of the Israelite army. Before the sun was up they crossed the Jordan River and attacked the camp of the Ammonites, scattering them in all directions. So the city of Jabesh-Gilead was saved.

Then Samuel called an assembly of all the tribes of Israel. "You asked for a king," he said, "and God has sent you one. There is not a man like him in all Israel." And Samuel pointed to Saul, standing head and shoulders above the crowd.

"If you keep God's commandments, both you and your king, it will be well with you," he said. "But if you do evil, you and your king shall be swept away."

Then Samuel took his horn of oil and anointed Saul again before all the people.

"Long live the king," the people shouted. "Long live King Saul!"

David's
Great-Grandmother Ruth

In the little town of Bethlehem in Judah there once lived a woman, named Naomi, with her husband and two sons. It came to pass that there was a famine in the land, and the family moved across the Jordan River to the land of Moab. There the boys grew up and married Moabite women, Orpah and Ruth. But trouble came to Naomi. First her husband, then both her sons died.

The famine in Judah was over by now. So Naomi set out for her old home in Bethlehem. Her daughters-in-law followed her.

"Turn back, my daughters," Naomi said to them. "Why should you go with me? I am old and poor. Return each of you to her mother's home. May God be kind to you as you have been to me and to my sons."

Then Orpah kissed her mother-in-law and went back to her people. But Ruth clung to Naomi and would not leave her.

Naomi said to her, "See, your sister-in-law is going back to her own people. Go with her."

But Ruth answered, "Entreat me not to leave you or to return from following after you. Wherever you go I will go. Where you live I will live. Your people shall be my people and your God my God. Only death shall part us."

Naomi saw that Ruth was determined to go with her, so she said no more. The two went on together and reached Bethlehem at the time of the barley harvest. The farmers with their families and servants were out in the fields, cutting and binding the ripe barley, loading it on donkeys and in ox carts. Those who had no fields of their own followed after the reapers, searching the fields for stalks that had been left behind. Gleaning, this was called.

Ruth said to Naomi, "Let me go out and glean in the fields."

"Go, my daughter," Naomi said to her.

It happened that the field to which Ruth came belonged to a rich farmer named Boaz, a relative of Naomi. At noon Boaz came down from Bethlehem to see how the work was getting on.

"The Lord be with you," he said to his servants.

"The Lord bless you," they answered.

Then he noticed Ruth and spoke to her kindly.

"Go to no other field," he said to her, "but stay close beside my servants. When you are thirsty drink of the water the men have drawn."

Ruth bowed and asked, "Why are you so kind to me, a stranger?"

Boaz answered, "I have been told of all that you have done for your mother-in-law since your husband died, how you left your father and your mother and the land where you were born, and came to our people whom you did not know. May the Lord God reward you for your good deeds."

At noon Boaz invited Ruth to share their meal. Before he left he said to his men, "Let her gather all the barley she wants, and do not be rude to her. Drop some handfuls of grain purposely for her to pick up."

That evening when Ruth beat out the stalks she had gathered, there was a full measure of barley to carry home to Naomi.

"Your daughter-in-law is better to you than seven sons," Naomi's old neighbors said to her.

All through the barley harvest and the wheat harvest Boaz watched Ruth as she worked in the fields. When the harvest was over, he asked her to be his wife. In time a son, Obed, was born to them.

Obed grew up and became the father of Jesse. And
Jesse had two daughters and eight sons. The youngest of
the sons was David.

David Meets
Samuel the Prophet

David, the young son of Jesse, tended his father's sheep
in the pasture up in the hills. He was a fine looking boy,
quick and brave. He could aim his slingshot at a spring-
ing lion and hit him between the eyes before his paw
came down on a lamb. He could play sweet music on his
shepherd harp. David's older brothers often left the farm
to fight with King Saul against the Philistines. But David
had to stay with the sheep.

Now Samuel, the prophet, was still living at this time,
an old, old man.

One day God said to him, "Samuel, I have chosen one
of Jesse's sons to be the next king of Israel. Take your
horn of oil and go up to Bethlehem to anoint him."

172

So Samuel took his horn of oil and set out for Jesse's home in Bethlehem. Jesse wondered what had brought the holy man to his house, but he did not ask. His wonder grew when Samuel asked him to bring his sons before him.

Eliab, the eldest, came first. He was tall and handsome. For a moment Samuel thought, "This is the man." But God said to him, "Do not look at his face or at his height. Man looks at the outside appearance, but God looks into the heart."

The second son came up.

"God has not chosen this one either," Samuel said.

So seven of Jesse's sons passed by.

Then Samuel asked, "Are these the only sons you have?"

"There is one more," Jesse answered, "the youngest, David. He is tending the sheep."

"Send for him," Samuel said, "I will not sit down to the feast until he comes."

So David was sent for. He ran all the way from the pasture. His cheeks were flushed and his eyes full of wonder when he stood before the holy man. The moment Samuel looked at David he said, "This is the one. The Lord has chosen him."

Solemnly Samuel raised his horn of oil and poured the oil on David's head. Then he went his way leaving the family wondering.

"Why has Samuel anointed David?" they asked. "What has God chosen him to be?"

From that day a change came over David. People said, "The spirit of God is in the boy."

Now when David played upon the harp his songs were all of God and of His goodness.

"I will praise the Lord with all my heart.
I will sing of His wonders."

David Plays for the King

There was great excitement on Jesse's farm. A messenger had come from King Saul asking Jesse to send his son David to the king.

"The king is sick," the messenger explained. "It is not a sickness of the body. Something is troubling him. He has become sad and fearful and will not leave his tent. They say your son is a skillful player on the harp. When a spell of sadness comes upon the king he shall play for him. It may be that the music will make him well."

So once more David was called from the sheep. Jesse loaded a donkey with bread and wine and a young kid, gifts for the king. And David set out. That same day he was brought before Saul. The brave king who had rescued Jabesh-Gilead and had led his people boldly against the Philistines now sat in a darkened tent with his head bowed low. Jonathan, the young prince, stood beside him.

"Play upon your harp," Jonathan said. "It may be that your playing will help him."

David put his hands to the strings and sweet music filled the tent.

For the first time Saul looked up. His eyes brightened.

"You please me," he said to David. "I will ask your father to let you stay on with me."

So David came to live with King Saul. Saul loved him greatly. Whenever the spell of sadness came upon the king, David played for him on his harp and the sadness would leave him.

David Fights a Giant

Once again the Philistines gathered to make war against Israel. Saul had to go to meet the enemy, and David returned to Bethlehem.

It was hard for David to stay quietly at home. He wanted to be fighting beside the king. So he was happy one day when his father said, "David, go down to the camp and see how your brothers are getting on."

David set out early in the morning. As he drew near the camp he heard a great shout. The Israelites were standing on one hill, the Philistines on another. A valley lay between them with a brook running through it. As David ran up, a giant strode out of the Philistine lines. He was more than ten feet tall and was dressed from head to foot in armor. A huge spear was in his hand. In a voice like thunder he shouted, "I challenge the armies of Israel. Send a man to fight with me. If he kills me, the Philistines will be your servants. If I kill him, the Israelites will be *our* servants."

The Israelite soldiers trembled.

"Who is this giant who comes to mock us?" David asked.

"He is Goliath, the Philistine," someone answered. "Each day for forty days he has given his challenge. No one dares to fight against him."

Then David said, "I will fight the man myself for he has mocked the army of the living God."

David was led at once to the king's tent. But Saul smiled when he saw him and shook his head.

"You cannot go up against this Philistine," he said. "You are little more than a boy and he has been a fighter from his youth."

But David spoke earnestly, "My king, once when I was with my father's sheep a lion came and snatched a lamb from the flock. I went after the lion and attacked him and saved the lamb. When the lion turned on me I seized him by his beard and killed him. The Lord who saved me from the lion will save me from the Philistine."

Then Saul said to David, "Go, and may the Lord be with you."

He gave the boy his own armor to put on, a brass helmet, a brass coat and breast plate, and a sword to hang at his side. David tried the armor on, then put it aside.

"I cannot walk in these. I am not used to them," he said.

He took his sling shot in his hand and ran out of the tent and down into the valley between the two armies. At the brook he stopped, picked up five smooth stones and put them into his bag. Then he ran on toward the Philistines.

Goliath, the giant, came forward cautiously with his

shield bearer before him. But when he saw that the Israelite champion was a rosy-cheeked boy with a sling shot, he laughed scornfully.

"Am I a dog that you come at me with sticks? Come and I will give your flesh to the beasts of the fields."

David answered, "You come to me with a sword and a spear, but I come to you in the name of the Lord God whom you have defied."

Quickly he put his hand into his bag, took out a stone and slung it. The stone flew straight to Goliath's head and sank into his forehead. Down went Goliath with his face to the ground. David ran up, drew the giant's sword out of his belt, and killed him.

When the Philistines saw that their champion was dead, they fled in terror. The Israelites pursued them all the way to the gates of their cities.

In Saul's tent David found Jonathan, the prince, waiting for him.

"I heard you when you talked to my father," Jonathan said. "I also saw the battle. Never have I met anyone so brave."

He took off the royal cloak which he wore and gave it to David together with his sword and bow. Then the two swore that they would be friends forever. From that day Jonathan and David loved each other like brothers.

Saul Turns Against David

David stayed on with the king. He became a captain of ten thousand men and won many victories against the Philistines. All Israel loved and praised him.

But suddenly a change came over Saul. It began one day when David was returning from battle. The women of the city went out to meet him, dancing and singing. Saul heard them and frowned, for the song that they sang was this:

> "Saul has slain his thousands
> But David his ten thousands."

"They are saying that David is ten times as brave a man as I am," Saul thought. "Soon they will be wanting David for their king instead of me."

From that time Saul watched David jealously. One day when David was playing for him on the harp, Saul lifted his spear and hurled it at him. The spear missed David and stuck in the wall. Then David realized that Saul meant to kill him and he fled from the palace.

From his hiding place David sent for Jonathan. "What have I done?" he said to the prince. "What wrong did I do your father that he seeks to kill me?"

Jonathan was full of sorrow for his friend. The two thought of a plan to find out whether it was safe for David to return.

"Hide in the field behind the stoneheap," Jonathan said. "The day after tomorrow I will come there with my young servant and shoot three arrows. Listen carefully when I send the boy to pick up the arrows. If I say to him, 'See, the arrows are on this side of you. Get them,' you will know that all is well. But if I say to the boy, 'See, the arrows are beyond you,' it will mean that you must escape."

The next day, at the Feast of the New Moon, David's place was empty.

"Why is it that the son of Jesse is not at the table?" Saul asked.

Jonathan answered, "I gave him permission to attend a family feast in Bethlehem."

Saul cried, "Do you not know that as long as David lives you will never be king? Go and fetch him that he may die."

Jonathan left the table in fierce anger and ate no food

all day. In the morning he went out to the field with his bow and arrows, taking a small boy with him.

"Run ahead," he said to the boy. "Find the arrows that I shoot."

As the boy ran, Jonathan called in a voice loud enough for David to hear, "Is not the arrow beyond you? Make haste! Be quick! Do not wait."

The boy picked up the arrows and brought them to his master, and Jonathan sent him back to the city.

When the boy was gone David arose from behind the stone heap and came over to Jonathan. The two friends kissed each other and wept.

"Go in peace," Jonathan said.

Then David arose and hurried on his way, and Jonathan returned to the city.

David Becomes
an Outlaw

Away David went, not waiting to take food or supplies with him, not even a sword.

High in the hills where bears and lions had their dens, there was a deep cave called the Cave of Adullam. Here David made his hideout.

Soon a band of bold and fearless men gathered about him. There were his brothers from Bethlehem. There were his three daring nephews, each as swift as a deer. There were bowmen who could shoot an arrow with either the right or the left hand. Everyone who was in trouble found his way to David. In time there were six hundred loyal men in his band.

The shepherds in the wilderness were glad to have David nearby. His men fought off the robber bands that came to steal their sheep. In return, the rich sheep owners sent David gifts of food, bread and meat, corn and grapes and figs. With David for a friend they knew their flocks were safe.

But David was never safe. Saul and his army pursued him from place to place and never gave him rest.

Once it happened that Saul came to the very cave where David was hiding. Saul's soldiers brought a great boulder and placed it before the entrance. Then they lay down to sleep, not knowing that behind them, deep in the mountain, were David and his men. During the night David crept up to the sleeping king. He was near enough to cut off the bottom of his robe. But he would not harm him.

In the morning, when Saul learned that David had spared his life, he was ashamed and returned to his home.

But the old fear and hate came back. Again the king went out to search for David. This time he took with him three thousand of his best fighters. In the wilderness of Ziph, they set up camp.

David did not wait for Saul to attack. Taking one of his nephews with him, he stole into Saul's camp in the night. The whole army lay asleep, the king, the soldiers, Abner the captain. Saul's spear was stuck in the ground near his head.

David's nephew whispered to him, "God has put your enemy into your power. I beg you, let me pin him to the earth with his own spear."

But again David spared Saul's life.

"God forbid that I should hurt him," he said to his nephew.

He took the king's spear and his jug of water and left the camp.

From the opposite hill David called across the valley. "Abner! What sort of man are you? Why have you not kept guard over the king? You deserve to die for failing to watch over your master."

Then David raised Saul's spear and jug above his head and called, "See where the king's spear is, and the jug of water that was at his head. Let one of your young men come over and get them."

The king recognized David's voice. "Is it you, my son David?" he asked.

David answered, "It is, O king. Why do you pursue me? What wrong have I done you? Why do you hunt me as men hunt wild birds in the mountains?"

Saul said, "I have done wrong and acted foolishly, my son David. Return. I will do you no more harm. Twice you have spared my life."

But David thought, "Today the king loves me. But tomorrow the old sickness will return and he will fear and hate me again. If I remain I shall surely be captured by him some day. There is but one thing to do. I must escape to the land of the Philistines. Then Saul will hunt for me no more."

So David took his faithful band and went over to the land of the Philistines. The Philistines gave him a place in the country to live in, and David and his men settled there and brought over their wives and children.

Often David led his men on raids against the Amalekites, but he never helped the Philistines fight against his own people, the people of Israel.

The Death of Saul and Jonathan

Now came the hardest time in David's life. He saw the Philistines gather together a great army and set out to fight against his own people, the Israelites. And there was nothing he could do to stop them.

Luckily the Philistine captains did not want David to go with them. "Let this fellow stay behind," they said. "Is he not the same David that killed our champion, Goliath? How do we know he will not turn against us in battle?"

So David remained behind, waiting anxiously for news of the battle. One day a man came running toward him, breathless, his clothes torn. He fell to the ground before David.

"Where do you come from?" David asked.

"I have escaped from the camp of Israel," the man answered.

"How did the battle go? Tell me."

"The Israelites fled from the battlefield. All of them have fallen. Saul and Jonathan are dead, slain on Mount Gilboa."

Then David wept aloud and mourned for Saul and Jonathan.

> Your beauty, O Israel, on the high places
> is slain!
> How are the mighty fallen!

David Becomes King

The time had come for David to return to his own land. He took his faithful men and their families and went up to the city of Hebron in Judah. The men of Judah asked David to be their king. But the rest of the tribes were divided. Some wanted David and some wanted one of the sons of Saul. And there was confusion and fighting. But in the end all the tribes of Israel came over to David's side.

"Behold," they said, "when Saul was our king it was you who led us against our enemies and brought us back victorious. We have heard how Samuel anointed you when you were a shepherd boy in Bethlehem. God has chosen you to be our king."

Then the elders poured oil on David's head just as Samuel had done long ago.

David, the shepherd, was Israel's king.

Now David remembered Jonathan who had been his loyal and beloved friend.

"Is anyone left of Jonathan's family to whom I may show kindness?" he asked.

An old servant of Saul answered. "There is a son still living. He is crippled in both his feet."

And he told the story of the lame prince.

Jonathan's son was five years old on the day his father died. He was playing with his nurse when someone came running with the news that Saul and Jonathan had been killed in battle. The nurse picked up the little prince and ran in fear. As she ran the boy fell out of her arms and was made lame. Now he was living on a farm with an old servant of his grandfather.

When King David heard the story of Jonathan's crippled son, he had him brought to the palace. The boy came before him trembling, fearful that the king would do him harm. But David spoke to him gently.

"Do not fear. I will show you kindness for the sake of Jonathan, your father. You shall be as one of my own sons and eat at my table."

Then he turned to Saul's servant. "I am giving the boy all the land that belonged to his grandfather, Saul. You and your sons are to farm it for him."

The old servant answered gladly, "I have many sons and servants. You may depend upon us to do just as you say."

So Jonathan's son came to live in the palace and was treated like David's own sons.

192

Jerusalem

High up on a mountain between the north and the south was the city of Jerusalem. All the land round about belonged to the Israelites, but Jerusalem was still in the hands of their enemies. No one had ever been able to take it.

David knew that unless this city in the middle of their

land belonged to Israel, his people would never be safe. So he took an army and went up against it.

The people of Jerusalem felt so safe in their city on the mountain top that they leaned over the walls and mocked at David.

"You shall never capture Jerusalem. Our city is so strong that our blind men and our lame can defend it."

But David had a plan of his own. He had discovered a secret tunnel that carried water into the city. Into the tunnel went two of his brave men. Up and up they climbed until they found themselves inside the city walls. At night they unlocked the gates and let the king and his army in.

So Jerusalem, which means city of peace, was taken by David, and became the capital of all the land.

In Jerusalem David set up a Tabernacle for the Ark of the Law, the Ark in which the Ten Commandments were kept. All the people of Israel gathered together to bring the Ark to its new home. They followed it, playing on harps and singing songs of thanks. So great was the joy that King David himself sang and danced before the Ark. Ever since that day Jerusalem has been our holy city.

David ruled for many years, a brave and a just king, loving God and serving Him. All his life he wrote beautiful songs in God's praise.

The Story of King Solomon

Solomon Is Born

King David stood on the roof of his palace looking down over the city. With him was the prophet Nathan.

"Behold," David said, "I live in this house of cedar wood while the Ark of God is in a tent. Let me build a beautiful house for God, a house of stone and cedar wood."

"Do what is in your heart," Nathan answered.

That night God spoke to Nathan, saying, "Go back to David, my servant, and tell him, 'You shall not build Me a house, for you have been a man of war. Behold, a son shall be born to you who will be a man of peace. His name will be Solomon. Your son, Solomon, shall build My Temple'."

Soon after this a son was born to David's wife, Bathsheba. David named the baby Solomon which means peace.

Little Solomon grew up in the palace with many older brothers. But none was so bright as he. Ask him any riddle. He would guess the answer. Speak to him in any language. He would understand. People from many nations came to Jerusalem, slaves and princes, carpenters and goldsmiths, merchants and sailors. Solomon spoke to them all, each in his own language.

Those who listened smiled and said, "Soon the boy will be learning the language of the beasts and birds."

That was just what Solomon wanted to do. He would bend over an ant heap and watch the long line of ants carrying bits of food to store away for the winter. He would listen to the cuckoo bird in the garden chatter with its mate. He would try to understand the animals in his father's stalls, the donkeys and oxen. Everything that was alive interested him.

As for God's law, Solomon knew it almost by heart, so that Nathan, the prophet, loved him greatly.

Of all his sons, David chose Solomon to be the king after him.

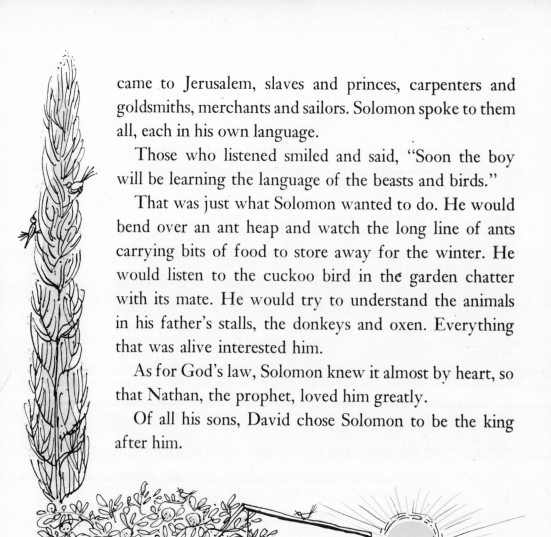

Solomon Makes a Wish

When the time came for David to die, he sent for Solomon and said to him, "My son, I am going the way of all on earth. Be strong, therefore, and prove yourself a man. Keep the commandments of the Lord your God. Serve Him in truth with all your soul and might."

That night God appeared to Solomon in a dream.

"Ask Me what you wish and it shall be given you," God said to him.

Solomon answered, "O God, You have made me king in my father's place. I am so young, and here is this great people that I must lead. Give me wisdom so that I may rule the people justly."

God was pleased with Solomon's answer and said to him, "Because you asked nothing for yourself but only for wisdom, you shall be wiser than any man that ever lived. And I will also give you what you did not ask for, riches and honor and long life."

The next morning, as Solomon sat on his throne judging the people, two women came before him, holding a

199

baby between them.

"O my king," the first one said, "this woman and I live in the same house. Each of us had a child. But her child died in the night as I lay asleep. Then she arose, took my living child from my side, and put her dead child in its place."

"No! No!" the other woman cried. "The living child is mine, and the dead child is hers."

But the first woman insisted, "No, the dead child is hers, and the living child is mine."

King Solomon turned to a servant.

"Fetch me a sword," he said.

When the sword was brought, Solomon said to the women, "Each of you says, 'The living child is mine.' There is but one thing to do. We will cut the child in two and give half to each of you."

Then the real mother, the one who had spoken first, cried out, "O my king, give her the living child. Only do not kill it."

But the other insisted, "It shall be neither mine nor hers. Divide it."

The king pointed to the woman who was willing to give up the child to save it. He said, "Give the child to her, for she is the mother."

Then the people of Israel knew that the wisdom of God was in their king.

The Temple Is Built

Four years went by. All that God had promised Solomon came to pass. The young king was not only wise, but rich and powerful and greatly honored. Israel lived at peace with all its neighbors. The time had come to build a House for the Ark of God, a holy Temple on Mount Zion.

Solomon sent a letter to his father's friend, Hiram, king of Tyre. "You know that my father David wanted to build a house in honor of the Lord our God. But the Lord said to him, 'Solomon, your son, shall build the house.' Now I am planning to begin the work. Send me cedar wood from Lebanon and I will pay you with wheat and wine and oil."

Hiram answered, "Blessed be the Lord your God who has given David so wise a son. I shall do all that you have asked."

Then Hiram sent his servants into the mountains of Lebanon. They cut down towering cedar trees, made them into rafts and floated them by sea to Jaffa. At Jaffa the Israelites cut the logs into beams, and carried them up to Jerusalem.

Other workers went up into the mountains around

Jerusalem and cut great blocks of stone for the foundations of the Temple. The stones were perfect, each of the proper size. No cutting or hammering was needed when they were brought up to Mount Zion. For Solomon had said, "Let no iron tool be heard in the Temple while it is being built. Iron is a metal used for weapons of war, and the Temple is to be a house of peace."

The Temple was completed at last. It stood on Mount Zion, strong and beautiful, its golden roof gleaming in the sun. The walls within were carved with palm trees and pomegranates and opening flowers. The floors were paved with gold. The inner room for the Ark was made of olive wood, covered inside and out with pure gold.

People came up to Jerusalem from all parts of the land.

The Ark of the Law was still in the tent where David had placed it. Now the *Kohanim*, the priests, carried the Ark to its new home. Young *Kohanim*, blowing silver trumpets, led the way. Levites followed, singing and playing on cymbals and harps. On went the *Kohanim* through joyful crowds gathered in the Temple courts, past the altar, up the broad stairs, and placed the Ark in the innermost room of the Temple, the Holy of Holies.

Then Solomon raised his hands toward heaven and prayed.

"O God, look down upon us in Your loving kindness. When Your people, Israel, come to this place to pray, answer their prayer. And if a stranger comes from a far land, send him help too. For You are God and King of all the earth."

For seven days the people feasted and sang and gave thanks to God. On the eighth day Solomon blessed them and sent them home, full of joy and gladness.

The Queen of Sheba

The fame of Solomon spread until it reached the distant
land of Sheba. Now the ruler over Sheba was a wise and
beautiful queen.

"I will go to Jerusalem to see this great king for myself," she said. "I will see whether he is really as wise as
men say."

So the queen of Sheba set out with a great company,
handsome youths and beautiful maidens, servants and
wise men, camels bearing spices and gold and precious
stones. For many weeks they traveled until they came at
last to Jerusalem.

Each day the queen of Sheba spent many hours with
Solomon. She sat beside him when he judged the people
and marveled at his understanding. They walked together
in the garden, talking of plants and birds, of beasts and
insects. Solomon knew every tree that grew, from the
towering cedars on Mount Lebanon to the little hyssop
that springs out of a crack in the rock.

They sat at banquets where food was served in golden dishes. While they ate, the queen asked Solomon riddles and watched to see how quick he was in answering.

One day the queen came to Solomon carrying two flowers in her hands.

"One of these flowers is real and one is not real," she said. "Tell me, which is the real one?"

The flowers looked exactly alike. Everyone waited for Solomon's answer. The room grew so quiet one could hear the bees buzzing in the garden.

"Open a window," Solomon said to a servant.

The window was opened and a bee flew in. It passed the first flower and alighted on the second.

Solomon turned to the queen, smiling, "The bee has given you the answer."

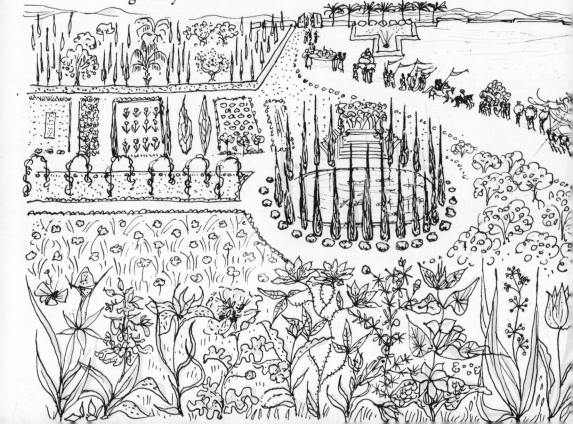

Sometimes the queen of Sheba asked Solomon questions that had long troubled her. "What is the beginning of wisdom? Where is the path that leads to happiness?" Solomon gave her many wise answers. They are all written down in the book of Proverbs.

So, many months passed by. One day the queen of Sheba visited the Temple in Solomon's company. It was the Festival of Sukkot. Crowds of joyous people were gathered in the courts. Smoke arose from the altars. Levites ascended the broad stairs, singing as they went. The sun shone on the golden roof of the Temple and the great bronze pillars.

Solomon said to the queen, "Beyond the pillars is the holy place, and within the holy place is the Holy of Holies."

"What is kept in the Holy of Holies?" the queen asked. "An image of your God?"

Solomon answered, "Our God cannot be seen. There is nothing in the Holy of Holies but the Ark with the tablets of God's law."

The queen pointed to the altars.

"Your priests make many offerings."

Solomon said to her, "Only one of the offerings is for Israel. The rest are for the other seventy nations. We pray that God may send blessings to all the peoples of the earth."

Then the queen of Sheba could contain herself no longer, and said to Solomon, "I heard in my own land of your greatness and your wisdom. But the half was not told me. Blessed be the Lord your God! Because the Lord loves Israel He has made you king to rule wisely and justly."

Then the queen of Sheba arose and returned to her own land.

Solomon ruled in Jerusalem for the rest of his life. As long as he lived there was peace in Israel.